IT's ABOUT TIME ®

HERFF JONES EDUCATION DIVISION

84 Business Park Drive, Armonk, NY 10504   Phone (914) 273-2233
Fax (914) 273-2227   Toll Free (888) 698-TIME (8463)   www.its-about-time.com

It's About Time, Founder
Laurie Kreindler

Creative/Art Director
John Nordland

Design/Production
Kadi Sarv
Murray Fuchs

Biology Reviewers
Dr. Arthur Eisenkraft
William H. Leonard
Philip Estrada
Marissa Hipol
Laura Hajdukiewicz

Project Editor
Ruta Demery

Project Managers
Barbara Zahm
John Nordland

Technical Art
Burmar Technical Corporation
Kadi Sarv

Illustrations
Tomas Bunk
Dennis Falcon

Photo Research
Jon Voss
Kadi Sarv
Jennifer Von Holstein

Safety Reviewers
Dr. Ed Robeck
Gregory Puskar

All student activities in this textbook have been designed to be as safe as possible, and have been reviewed by professionals specifically for that purpose. As well, appropriate warnings concerning potential safety hazards are included where applicable to particular activities. However, responsibility for safety remains with the student, the classroom teacher, the school principals, and the school board.

Printed and bound in the United States of America

ISBN #1-58591-275-1

1 2 3 4 5 VH 08 07 06 05 04

Table of Contents

A Vote For Ecology   Chapter 1

Scenario   1

Chapter Challenge, Criteria   2

Activity One: Diversity in Living Things   4

Activity Two: Who Eats Whom?   16

Activity Three: Energy Flow in Ecosystems   24

Activity Four: Factors Affecting Population Size   31

Activity Five: Competition Among Organisms   40

Activity Six: Succession in Communities   48

Activity Seven: The Water Cycle   55

Activity Eight: Photosynthesis, Respiration, and the Carbon Cycle   63

Activity Nine: The Nitrogen and Phosphorous Cycles   69

Biology At Work   78

A Highway Through The Past   Chapter 2

Scenario, Chapter Challenge   80

Criteria   81

Activity One: Adaptations   82

Activity Two: Is It Heredity or the Environment?   92

Activity Three: Natural Selection   99

Activity Four: The Fossil Record   109

Activity Five: Mass Extinction and Fossil Records   119

Biology At Work   126

Glossary   127

Charts, Graphs, Tables   132

Index   133

Acknowledgments

ACTIVE BIOLOGY
PRIMARY AND CONTRIBUTING AUTHORS

Active Biology Writers

Bob Ritter

Consultant, *Active Biology* and *Active Physics*

Bob Ritter is presently the principal of Holy Trinity High School in Edmonton, Alberta. Dr. Ritter began his teaching career in 1973. Since then he has had a variety of teaching assignments. He has worked as a classroom teacher, Science Consultant, and Department Head. He has also taught Biological Science to student teachers at the University of Alberta. He is presently involved with steering committees for "At Risk High School Students" and "High School Science."

Dr. Ritter is author of many publications. He has written numerous biology textbooks and laboratory manuals for middle and high school students during the past 25 years. He has also developed a variety of professional teaching materials. These include *Teaching Controversial Issues, Learning Strategies*, and *Teacher and Student Perceptions about Alternative Assessment.*

Dr. Ritter is frequently a presenter and speaker at national and regional conventions across Canada and the United States. He has initiated many creative projects, including establishing a science-mentor program in which students would have an opportunity to work with professional biologists. In 1993 Dr. Ritter received the Prime Minister's Award for Science and Technology Teaching. He has also been honored as Teacher of the Year and with an Award of Merit for contribution to science education.

Dr. Ritter was consultant and contributing writer to the *Active Biology* unit. He also developed the assessment strategies and rubrics for the *Active Physics* teacher's guides.

Ruta Demery

Project Editor and Contributing Writer, *EarthComm, Active Physics, Active Chemistry*, and *Active Biology*

Ruta Demery is an editorial consultant. She has been engaged in educational publishing for over 30 years. She has also worked as a classroom science and mathematics teacher in both middle school and high school.

She has participated in the development and publishing of numerous innovative mathematics and science books. She has also been a contributing writer for a variety of mathematics and science textbooks and teacher's guides. She brings to her work a strong background in curriculum development and a keen interest in student assessment. When time permits, she also leads workshops to familiarize teachers with new classroom materials.

Ruta Demery is presently involved in editorial consulting on several National Science Foundation (NSF) projects. She was the project editor for *EarthComm, Active Physics, Active Chemistry*, and *Active Biology*. She was also a contributing writer for *Active Physics* and *Active Biology*, both students' and teachers' editions.

Active Biology Consultants

Dr. Arthur Eisenkraft
Project Director of *Active Physics* and *Active Chemistry*. Past President of the National Science Teachers Association (NSTA)

William H. Leonard, Ph.D.
Clemson University
Professor of Education and Biology
Co-Author *Bio Comm*

Philip Estrada
Biology Teacher Hollywood High School, LAUSD

Marissa Hipol
Biology Teacher Hollywood High School, LAUSD

Laura Hajdukiewicz
Biology Teacher, Andover, MA

You can do Biology. Here are the reasons why.

Biology is life! Biology gives you knowledge about nature, the impact it has on you and the impact you have on it. Are you interested in the incredible diversity of organisms that live on Earth and how they have evolved? Here is how you are going to learn about this, and other topics in biology.

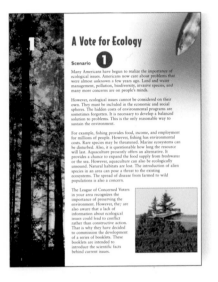

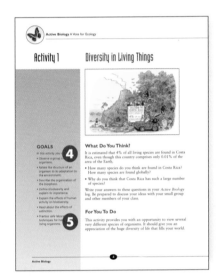

❶ Scenario

Each chapter begins with a relevant event or situation that places biology in the context of an everyday experience you may be familiar with. Chances are you can relate to each of these scenarios but never thought about the biology involved in them!

❷ Chapter Challenge

This feature presents you with a challenge that you can expect to complete by the end of the chapter. As you progress through the chapter you will accumulate all the knowledge you need to successfully complete the challenge.

❸ Criteria

Before you begin the challenge, and the chapter, you will be part of the decision-making process as to the standards your work will be held to. You will know exactly how your work will be graded and what you need to do to be successful!

❹ What Do You Think?

Find out how much you already know by answering the questions at the beginning of each activity. This is a great way to explore and discuss the ideas you have about a topic without being concerned about having the "right" answer.

❺ For You To Do

Research tells us that the best way to learn is by doing. You may already know this from other learning situations such as sports or hobbies. In *Active Biology* you will take an active role in your learning by participating in scientific inquiry and developing answers and conclusions.

❻ BioTalk

BioTalk further develops and explains the biology concepts learned from the investigations. Photographs and illustrations visually explain the concepts presented for better understanding of the biology in your world.

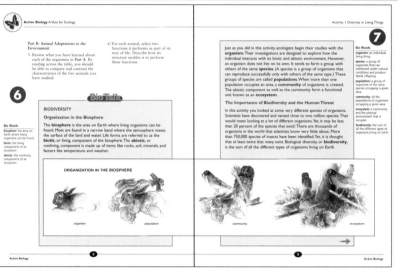

⑦ BioWords

BioWords highlights the important terms you need to know for maximum understanding. Key terms are redefined and further explained for you to make reading and comprehension easier.

⑧ Reflecting on the Activity and the Challenge

This feature provides a brief summary of the activity and helps you make connections between the activity and the challenge. This helps you take an active role in the process of learning as you reflect on what is learned and apply it to a larger goal.

⑨ Biology to Go

Here are exercises, problems, and questions that help you further develop your understanding of the activity and relate it to the chapter challenge.

⑩ Inquiring Further

This feature helps you organize and synthesize the knowledge you have mastered from the chapter activities to complete the challenge successfully.

⑪ Biology at Work

Biology is an integral part of many fascinating careers. This feature introduces some people working in different fields that involve the principles of biology and how they are making a difference in our world.

Would you like to develop a booklet to help people to decide how to vote? Perhaps you would like to express your opinions in a town-hall meeting. *Active Biology* has fascinating challenges that ask you to use your creativity, interests, and expertise to complete challenges in the same way professionals do.

When scientists, artists, writers, and engineers are hired to solve a problem, their first responsibility is to understand the nature of the assignment. Often, they must do research to better acquaint themselves with the topic. The person assigning the job has a sense of what is needed, but does not know exactly what the final product will be.

As you complete the chapter challenges, you will begin to combine your science knowledge with your other interests and create something that will represent the best efforts of you and your team. You will be learning about biology. You will learn about the incredible variety of organisms that inhabit the earth and how they have adapted to their environment. You will investigate competition among organisms and the process of natural selection. You will discover the factors that affect population size. And you will understand that the extinction of one organism can affect an entire ecosystem.

This course that will engage you in asking the types of questions that scientist ask; will have you explore the world in the way that scientists explore the world; and will require you to show that you really understand the meaning and implications of the scientific principles.

You will begin to think like a scientist.

Be creative, be curious, explore, and discover.

A Vote for Ecology

Scenario

Many Americans have begun to realize the importance of ecological issues. Americans now care about problems that were almost unknown a few years ago. Land and water management, pollution, biodiversity, invasive species, and many more concerns are on people's minds.

However, ecological issues cannot be considered on their own. They must be included in the economic and social spheres. The hidden costs of environmental programs are sometimes forgotten. It is necessary to develop a balanced solution to problems. This is the only reasonable way to sustain the environment.

For example, fishing provides food, income, and employment for millions of people. However, fishing has environmental costs. Rare species may be threatened. Marine ecosystems can be disturbed. Also, it is questionable how long the resource will last. Aquaculture presently offers an alternative. It provides a chance to expand the food supply from freshwater or the sea. However, aquaculture can also be ecologically unsound. Natural habitats are lost. The introduction of alien species in an area can pose a threat to the existing ecosystems. The spread of disease from farmed to wild populations is also a concern.

The League of Concerned Voters in your area recognizes the importance of preserving the environment. However, they are also aware that a lack of information about ecological issues could lead to conflict rather than constructive action. That is why they have decided to commission the development of a series of booklets. These booklets are intended to introduce the scientific facts behind current issues.

Chapter Challenge

Your challenge is to create a booklet addressing one current issue. These booklets will be provided to the public. The League hopes that this will produce an informed public, who is better able to decide how to vote on any given issue. Before you begin, you will need to decide which audience you are targeting. You may choose to write your booklet geared to adult voters, teenagers, or a child. Regardless of which you choose, it is assumed that the readers will be non-specialists and the text should be written with this in mind. The booklets should be easily understood by your target audience.

In producing your booklet, you should:

• identify and research one current issue that threats the environment;

• provide the relevant data on the issue;

• draw attention to areas where data may be weak or lacking;

• interpret the data and indicate the limits of the interpretation.

In providing the science behind the issue, you should:

• identify the roles and importance of consumers, producers, and decomposers in an ecosystem;

• explain how matter is cycled and energy flows through ecosystems;

• provide the meaning and the importance of biodiversity;

• describe how changes in an ecosystem are determined and how they can be analyzed;

• tell how fluctuations in size of a population are determined by birth, death, immigration, and emigration.

Criteria

How will your booklet be graded? What qualities should a good booklet have? Discuss these matters with your small group and with your class. You may decide some or all of the following qualities are important:

• significance of the issue identified;

• completeness and accuracy of the ecology principles presented;

• merit of the interpretations suggested;

• readability of the booklet;

• design and layout of the booklet.

You may have additional qualities that you would like to include. Once you have determined the criteria that you wish to use, you will need to decide on how many points should be given to each criterion. Your teacher may wish to provide you with a sample rubric to help you get started.

Activity 1   Diversity in Living Things

GOALS

In this activity you will:

- Observe a group of diverse organisms.

- Relate the structure of an organism to its adaptation to the environment.

- Describe the organization of the biosphere.

- Define biodiversity and explain its importance.

- Explain the effects of human activity on biodiversity.

- Read about the effects of extinction.

- Practice safe laboratory techniques for handling living organisms.

What Do You Think?

It is estimated that 4% of all living species are found in Costa Rica, even though this country comprises only 0.01% of the area of the Earth.

- How many species do you think are found in Costa Rica? How many species are found globally?

- Why do you think that Costa Rica has such a large number of species?

Write your answers to these questions in your *Active Biology* log. Be prepared to discuss your ideas with your small group and other members of your class.

For You To Do

This activity provides you with an opportunity to view several very different species of organisms. It should give you an appreciation of the huge diversity of life that fills your world.

Part A: Observing Animal Diversity

1. With your teacher, review the guidelines concerning the proper handling of laboratory animals. Follow these guidelines carefully.

2. In your *Active Biology* log make an enlarged copy of the table shown below. The table should extend across two facing pages. Each of the 13 spaces should allow for several lines of writing.

3. In the *Characteristics* column, copy the words in italics from each of the following questions. The 13th space is for any other observations you make. All the specimens of one animal species and the materials and equipment needed for observing them are arranged at the station. Each team will have a turn at each station. Record only your observations, not what you have read or heard about the organism.

   1 What is the *habitat* of the animal? Does it live in water, on land, or both?

2 Is *body symmetry* radial (symmetry about a center) or bilateral (the left and the right sides of the body are mirror images)?

3 Does the animal have a *skeleton* (a structure that supports the organism's body)? If it does, is it an endoskeleton (on the inside) or an exoskeleton (on the outside)?

4 Is the animal's body *segmented* or is it *unsegmented*?

Several of the activities that follow involve the use of organisms in water. The water that the organisms are in should be considered a contaminant. Tables, equipment, and hands should be washed carefully so that germs are not inadvertently passed to people.

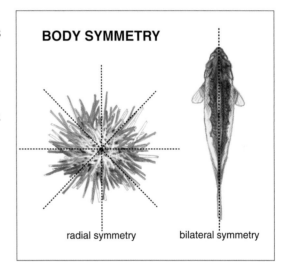

BODY SYMMETRY

radial symmetry   bilateral symmetry

Comparing Animals					
Characteristics	Hydra	Planarian	Earthworm	Hermit Crab	Frog
1					
2					
3					
13					

5 Which type of *digestive cavity* does the animal have, a sac (only one opening) or a tube (open at both ends)?

6 Does it have *paired appendages*?

7 How does the animal *obtain oxygen*? Through lungs, gills, skin, or a combination of these?

8 Are any *sense organs* visible? If so, what types and where?

9 How does the animal *move* from one place to another?

10 Does it make any types of *movement* while it remains more or less in one spot?

11 How does the animal *capture* and take in *food*?

12 How does it react when *touched* lightly with a small brush?

Station 1: Observing Hydras

1. Place a single hydra in a small watch glass with some of the same water in which it has been living. Wait until the animal attaches itself to the dish and extends its tentacles. Then slowly add a few drops of a daphnia culture with a dropping pipette.

2. Touch the hydra gently with a soft brush. Observe its reactions.

3. Examine a prepared slide of a lengthwise (longitudinal) section of a hydra under a compound microscope. Try to determine the presence or absence of a skeleton and of a digestive system.

Station 2: Observing Planarians

1. Place one or two planarians in a watch glass containing pond or aquarium water. Add a small piece of fresh raw liver. Observe using a stereomicroscope or hand lens.

As you move among the stations, keep your hands away from your mouth and eyes. Wash your hands well after the activity.

2. Use a compound microscope to examine cross sections of a planarian. Examine whole mounts with a stereomicroscope. Determine the presence or absence of a skeleton and a digestive system.

Station 3: Observing Earthworms

1. Pick up a live earthworm and hold it gently between your thumb and forefinger. Observe its movements. Do any regions on the body surface feel rough? If so, examine them with a hand lens.

2. Place a worm on a damp paper towel. Watch it crawl until you determine its anterior (front) and posterior (back) ends. Use a hand lens to see how the ends differ. Describe.

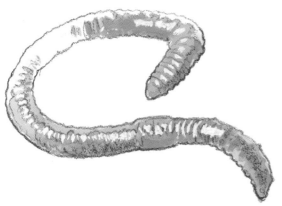

3. Place an earthworm on loose soil and observe its movements as it burrows.

4. Examine a model or a diagram of a cross section and lengthwise section of the earthworm's body.

Station 4: Observing Hermit Crabs

1. Observe the movements of the appendages and the pattern of locomotion (movement from one place to another) of a living land hermit crab. Observe the antennae. Touch them gently with a soft brush. Note the animal's reaction.

If you are observing a live crab in your classroom, keep your fingers away from the crab's pincers.

2. Place a small piece of food from the food dish in with the hermit crab. Observe how the hermit crab eats.

Station 5: Observing Frogs

1. Observe the breathing movements of a frog while it is not moving.

2. Observe the variety of movements of a live frog.

3. If possible, observe a frog capturing its food and feeding.

Wash your hands thoroughly before leaving the laboratory.

If you are handling a live frog in the classroom, do not rub your eyes. Wash your hands immediately after handling.

Part B: Animal Adaptations to the Environment

1. Review what you have learned about each of the organisms in **Part A**. By reading across the table, you should be able to compare and contrast the characteristics of the five animals you have studied.

a) For each animal, select two functions it performs as part of its way of life. Describe how its structure enables it to perform these functions.

Bio Talk

BIODIVERSITY

Organization in the Biosphere

The **biosphere** is the area on Earth where living organisms can be found. Most are found in a narrow band where the atmosphere meets the surface of the land and water. Life forms are referred to as the **biotic**, or living, component of the biosphere. The **abiotic**, or nonliving, component is made up of items like rocks, soil, minerals, and factors like temperature and weather.

Bio Words

biosphere: the area on Earth where living organisms can be found

biotic: the living components of an ecosystem

abiotic: the nonliving components of an ecosystem

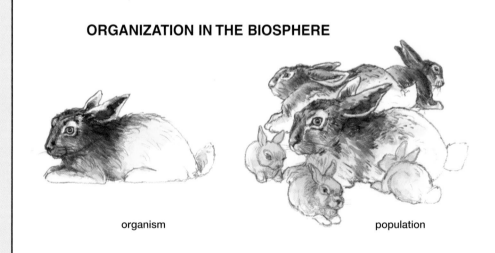

ORGANIZATION IN THE BIOSPHERE

organism   population

Just as you did in this activity, ecologists begin their studies with the **organism**. Their investigations are designed to explore how the individual interacts with its biotic and abiotic environment. However, an organism does not live on its own. It tends to form a group with others of the same **species**. (A species is a group of organisms that can reproduce successfully only with others of the same type.) These groups of species are called **populations**. When more than one population occupies an area, a **community** of organisms is created. The abiotic component as well as the community form a functional unit known as an **ecosystem**.

The Importance of Biodiversity and the Human Threat

In this activity you looked at some very different species of organisms. Scientists have discovered and named close to two million species. That would mean looking at a lot of different organisms. Yet, it may be less than 20 percent of the species that exist! There are thousands of organisms in the world that scientists know very little about. More than 750,000 species of insects have been identified. Yet, it is thought that at least twice that many exist. Biological diversity, or **biodiversity**, is the sum of all the different types of organisms living on Earth.

Bio Words

organism: an individual living thing

species: a group of organisms that can interbreed under natural conditions and produce fertile offspring

population: a group of organisms of the same species occupying a given area

community: all the populations of organisms occupying a given area

ecosystem: a community and the physical environment that it occupies

biodiversity: the sum of all the different types of organisms living on Earth

community   ecosystem

Unfortunately, many organisms are disappearing. This is partly due to alterations of habitats. The result is a decrease in biodiversity. Ecosystems with a large number of different types of organisms are quite stable. Ecosystems with a small number of different organisms are less stable. Humans are partly responsible for this change. As the human population grows it occupies more land. This infringes on or destroys the habitats of many organisms.

Smog is also hazardous to people. This is especially true of those with respiratory problems, the elderly, and children. People have died from the effects of smog.

The smog created by automobiles and industry is killing many types of trees over a wide area of southern California. The needles of ponderosa pines, for example, gradually turn brown. The tops of palm trees have only small tufts. When this happens, photosynthesis is greatly reduced. The plants die. The Everglades National Park in southern Florida depends on a slowly moving sheet of water. The water flows from north to south. Drainage ditches built at the northern edge of the Everglades have decreased the flow of water over the entire area. As a result, many alligator holes have dried up. These holes helped to contain fires in the Everglades. Now, destructive fires are more frequent in this national park.

Tropical rainforests are the most diverse ecosystems on Earth. They are home for many different species. Two-thirds of the world's species are located in the tropics and subtropics. The cutting of trees in the rainforests today has grown at a rapid rate. The trees are cut for lumber, grazing land, and other uses. This loss of habitat is destroying many species every day. Nearly half of the Earth's species of plants, animals, and microorganisms will become extinct, be gone forever, or be severely threatened, during the next 25 years.

To find a similar rate of **extinction** (loss of species), you need to go back 65 million years. That was the end of the Cretaceous period when dinosaurs and other organisms disappeared. Because there are more

Bio Words

extinction: the permanent disappearance of a species from Earth species today than there were then, the absolute number of species lost will be greater now. Hundreds of species of plants and animals are threatened today. They include the whooping crane and some rare pitcher plants. Extinction is a natural process. However, the process has been speeded up because humans have changed whole ecosystems.

In tropical regions, humans are cutting down, burning, or otherwise damaging the rainforests. Extinction of many species as well as change in global climate are some of the effects of this deforestation.

Why is biodiversity important? Why does it matter if whooping cranes and pitcher plants become extinct? One argument comes from genetics. In a field of crop plants planted by humans, all the plants are genetically similar. They have all inherited the same characteristics.

About 90% of the world's food comes from 15 species of plants. Three of them are corn, wheat, and rice. However, there are over 10,000 known species of cereals.

If one individual gets a disease, all the plants may die. In a wild population a vast pool of genetic characteristics are available. This means that some of the plants could resist the disease. Therefore, not all the plants would be destroyed. The extinction of each wild population erases genetic material that could mean healthy crops and animals. Once extinction occurs, the genetic material is gone forever.

A second argument is related to the fact that simple ecosystems are unstable. Think of a field of corn as a simplified ecosystem. Suppose all the corn dies. This means that the whole ecosystem would collapse. The simpler the ecosystem, the easier it is to disrupt its balance. The fewer the species, the easier it is to upset an ecosystem. New species are evolving all the time. However, the process is very slow compared to the rate at which humans are able to cause species to become extinct. Each time a species becomes extinct, the biosphere is simplified a little more. It becomes more difficult to maintain the stable biosphere on which all life depends.

A third argument comes from research on plants. The island of Madagascar, off the east coast of Africa, is the only known habitat of the Madagascar periwinkle. This plant produces two chemicals not produced by other plants. Both of these chemicals are used to fight Hodgkin's disease, a leukemia-like disease. As the human population on Madagascar grew, the habitat for the periwinkle shrank. The periwinkle almost became extinct. Fortunately, botanists collected and grew some of these plants before they were gone forever. The medicines made from the Madagascar periwinkle are worth millions of dollars each year. They also help many people with Hodgkin's disease to live longer. These medicines never would have been known if the plant had become extinct.

Extinction Can Cause a "Domino Effect"

Every organism in an ecosystem is connected to all the other organisms. The reduction in biodiversity caused by the extinction of a single species can cause a "domino effect." The removal of one part from an ecosystem, like the removal of a moving part from a car, can cause the collapse of an entire food chain. If a species acts as a predator, it keeps the population of its prey in check. If a species is prey, it provides an important food source.

For example, sea otters were over-hunted along the Pacific coasts of Asia and North America. This removed the main predator of the sea urchin. Predictably, the number of sea urchins grew rapidly. Sea urchins eat kelp, a form of seaweed. As the number of sea urchins grew, the amount of kelp declined. As a result, the fish that relied on the kelp for habitat and food were reduced in number.

Sea otters very nearly became extinct due to hunting pressure. For humans, killing the sea otters for their fur resulted in a decline in a valuable fishery. Where the sea otter has been reintroduced, sea urchin populations have fallen, kelp beds are being re-established, and the number of fish is increasing.

Restoring the Balance Is a Difficult Task

Introducing the sea otter to the Pacific northwest is an example of an attempt to restore a natural balance. It is not always easy to do. Conservationists have also tried to restore the whooping crane. In spring, whooping cranes fly north to live in the marshes and swamps of the prairies and the Canadian north. There they eat crayfish, fish, small mammals, insects, roots, and berries. Efforts by the United States and Canada have helped increase the population from a low of 14 individuals in 1940 to 183 in 1999. The whooping crane may be a success story, and it may not. Chemical pesticides were the original human threat to the crane. However, it was already struggling.

During the fur trade southern sea otters were hunted to near extinction. They are still a threatened species, and may very well be endangered.

Once widespread throughout North America, the whooping crane wild population dipped to just 15 birds in 1937. Through conservation efforts the whooping crane has begun a slow recovery. However, coastal and marine pollution, illegal hunting, and the draining of wetlands continue to threaten the species.

Cranes must fly a long way between their summer homes in the north and their winter homes on the Gulf of Mexico. Along the way they are vulnerable to hunting and accidents. In addition, the whooping crane reproduces very slowly. Each year females produce two eggs, however, only one will mature. The first fledgling to crawl from the egg kills its brother or sister. This ensures there will be enough food for the survivor. However, it is very difficult for the species to increase its numbers.

Scientists do not understand all the relationships between species ecosystems. They cannot predict what will happen if biodiversity is reduced, even by one species. If one species becomes extinct, it could be disastrous. The extent of the disaster may not be known until later. Sometimes the balance cannot be restored.

Reflecting on the Activity and the Challenge

In this activity you observed several very different living organisms. You then discovered that there are millions of other different organisms alive on Earth. There are reasons why it is important to make sure that these organisms do not disappear forever from the Earth. For your **Chapter Challenge** you may choose to research an issue that relates to the disappearance of a given species. You can now explain why it is important to maintain biological diversity. Whether or not your issue deals with biodiversity, the public still needs to understand why biological diversity should concern them. You need to provide the meaning and importance of biodiversity.

14

Biology to Go

1. Choose and identify two very different ecosystems.

    a) For each, name some of the populations that might be found in each community.

    b) Describe some of the abiotic factors that could affect each population.

2. What is biodiversity?

3. Explain how humans can influence biodiversity by changing the environment.

4. Why is maintaining biodiversity important?

5. a) Give an example of an ecosystem that has a high biodiversity.

    b) Give an example of an ecosystem that has a low biodiversity.

6. Choose an organism other than one that you studied in this activity. List at least three structures that have helped the organism adapt to its environment. Describe how each helps the organism live in its ecosystem.

Inquiring Further

1. The passenger pigeon and the human influence

Just over a century ago, the passenger pigeon was the most numerous species of bird on Earth. In the Eastern United States they numbered in the billions, more than all other species of North American birds combined. On September 1, 1914, at 1:00 PM the last surviving passenger pigeon died at the age of 29. Research and report on how humans were involved in the extinction of the passenger pigeon.

2. Extinction is forever

Humans were directly responsible for the extinction of passenger pigeons. However, this bird is not the only organism that has been threatened by humans. Research and report on another organism whose existence has been or is endangered by humans.

White rhinos are so large and powerful that in nature they must give way only to the elephant. Yet, humans are a major threat to their existence.

Activity 2

Who Eats Whom?

GOALS

In this activity you will:

- Distinguish between a food chain and a food web.
- Explain the roles of the producers, consumers, and decomposers.
- Understand the meanings of autotroph, heterotroph, herbivore, carnivore, and omnivore.
- Recognize the dependence of organisms on one another in an ecosystem.

What Do You Think?

You have probably heard the question, "If a tree falls in a forest and there is no one there to hear it, does it make a noise?"

- In ecology you might ask the question, "If a tree falls in a forest and there is no one there to haul it away, what happens to it?"

Write your answer to this question in your *Active Biology* log. Be prepared to discuss your ideas with your small group and other members of your class.

For You To Do

In this activity you will have an opportunity to explore how organisms in an ecosystem are dependent on one another.

16

Part A: A Food Chain

1. Look at the organisms in the pictures on the right.

   a) Link the names of the organisms together by the words "is eaten by."

   b) Show the relationship between the organisms as a linked word diagram or chain.

   c) Use arrows to show the direction in which food energy moves in the food chain you constructed in **Part (b)**.

   d) Identify the producer in the food chain.

   e) Identify the consumers in the food chain.

   f) Which consumer is a herbivore (feeds on plants)?

   g) Which consumers are carnivores (feed on other animals)?

   h) What elements are missing from this food chain?

Part B: A Food Web

1. Your teacher will provide you with a card that names an organism, what it does, what it eats, and what it is eaten by. You will also be given a name tag with your organism's name on it.

   Read your card and attach your "name" tag where others can readily identify you.

2. Clear a large area in your classroom, or find another large open area in or near your school. Form a large circle.

snake

grasshopper

frog

green plant

hawk

3. Obtain a big ball of string, about 35 m in length. Give the ball of string to one of the students.

4. The first student will say what organism he/she represents. Also, the student will indicate what the organism eats and what it is eaten by. The ball of string is then directed to one of students who represents the predator or the prey.

   a) As the game progresses, what appears to be forming in the center of the circle?

5. Suppose one organism is removed from the circle. Your teacher will direct you which organism will be removed.

a) What happens to the web that was created?

b) How does the removal of an organism impact on the other organisms in the circle?

6. Suppose that your circle has only a few organisms.

   a) What would happen to the web in this case if one of the organisms were removed?

   b) In which situation, a large or small "circle" of organisms, does the removal of an organism have a greater impact?

BioTalk

Bio Words

food chain: a series of organisms through which food energy is passed in an ecosystem

food web: a complex relationship formed by interconnecting food chains in an ecosystem representing the transfer of energy through different levels

autotroph: an organism that is capable of obtaining its energy (food) directly from the physical environment

heterotroph: an organism that must obtain its energy from autotrophs or other heterotrophs

producer: an organism that is capable of making its own food

consumer: a heterotrophic organism

herbivore: a heterotroph that feeds exclusively on plant materials

Food Chains and Webs

A bat ate a mosquito that had bitten a coyote that had eaten a grasshopper that had chewed a leaf. All these living things make up a **food chain.** A food chain is a step-by-step sequence that links together organisms that feed on each other. The story, however, is incomplete. It does not mention that many animals other than coyotes eat grasshoppers and mosquitoes bite other animals. It also does not consider that coyotes and bats eat and are eaten by a great many other living things. When you consider that the kind of plant a grasshopper might eat may also be eaten by various other consumers, you start to build a picture that links together a whole community of living things. Those links resemble a **food web** rather than a food chain. A food web is a series of interconnected food chains or feeding relationships. The diagram shows how members of a community interact in a food web.

Organisms in the Food Web

Autotrophs are organisms that are capable of obtaining their energy (food) directly from the environment. Most autotrophs obtain their energy through the process of photosynthesis. In this process solar energy is converted into a form of energy that can be used by the organism. **Heterotrophs** obtain their energy from autotrophs or other heterotrophs. For this reason autotrophs, the organisms that "make" the food, are called **producers**. In the diagram, grass, vegetables, and trees represent the producers. The heterotrophs are called **consumers**. **Herbivores** are first-order consumers. They feed directly on the plants. These organisms are removed by just one step

THE FOOD WEB

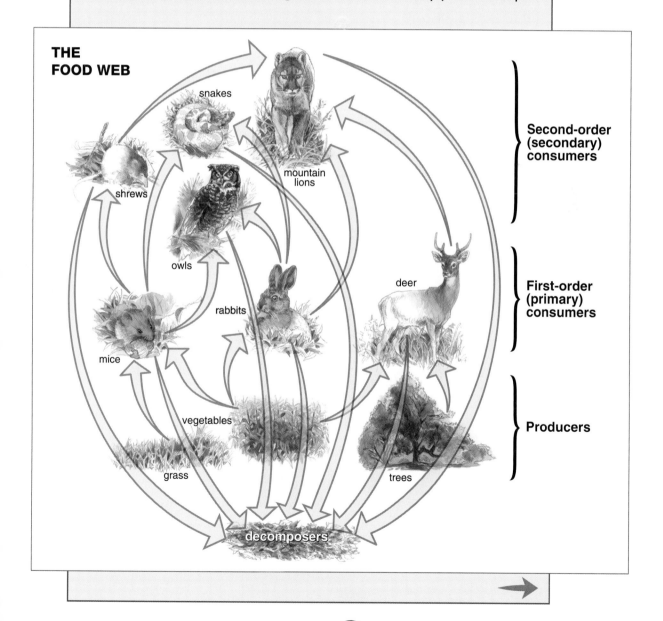

snakes

mountain lions

shrews

owls

rabbits

deer

mice

vegetables

grass

trees

decomposers

Second-order (secondary) consumers

First-order (primary) consumers

Producers

19

Bio Words

carnivore: an animal that feeds exclusively on other animals

omnivore: a heterotroph that feeds on both plant materials and animals

decomposers: organisms that break down the remains or wastes of other organisms to obtain their nutrients

in the food chain from the producers. In this example, they include mice, rabbits, and deer. **Carnivores** are second-order consumers. They feed on the animals that eat other plants. The owl and the mountain lion are just two examples of carnivores. **Omnivores** eat both plants and animals. A human is an example of an omnivore.

There is another group of organisms in the food web that is so important that these organisms are often treated as a separate group. They are the **decomposers**. They break down the complex organic molecules that are found in the wastes and bodies of other organisms. They do this to obtain food energy for their own use. In the process, they release nutrients back into the ecosystem. Bacteria and fungi make up most of the decomposers.

Alternative Pathways Maintain Stability in Food Webs

The alternative pathways in a food web help maintain the stability of the living community. If the rabbits in some area decrease in number, perhaps because of some disease, the owls might be expected to go hungry. However, this is not the case. The rabbits eat less vegetation. Hence, the greater number of plants produces more fruits, and seeds and furnishes better hiding places for mice. Soon a larger population of mice is present. The owls transfer their attention from rabbits to

The food habits of rabbits vary depending on location, time of year, and species of rabbit. They generally prefer to eat tender, green vegetation. They also eat leaves, bark, seeds, and even fruit of woody plants. Rabbits begin feeding in the evening and continue throughout the night.

mice. This reduces the danger for surviving rabbits, and these primary consumers have a better chance to rebuild their numbers. The greater the number of alternative pathways a food web has, the more stable is the community of living things which make up the web.

Owls are nighttime (nocturnal) birds of prey. Owls feed entirely on living animals. They eat everything from insects to mammals as large as rabbits. The size of the prey is proportional to the size of the owl.

Only a few of the possible offspring of a plant or animal survive to reproduce. Of all the seeds a plant forms, all but a few are eaten by animals. Some die from diseases. Others are killed by poor weather conditions. This can happen either as seeds or somewhat later in life, as young plants that have not yet formed seeds of their own.

Humans are so used to thinking of the welfare of their own species, that they tend to regard as "wasted" all the offspring that do not survive. But there is another side to the picture. For one thing, the world lacks space for so many individuals of any one kind. Also, these individuals are needed as food by a great variety of consumers. Without the fruits, seeds, young plants, and foliage, the primary consumers could not exist. Without the primary consumers, the plants would die. They would become overcrowded or lack nutrients. Without the primary consumers, the secondary consumers would be reduced in numbers because of competition, or would become extinct. Without waste from plants and animals, including dead remains, the decomposers would not be able to get their nutrients. Without decomposers, nutrients that the producers require would not be returned to the soil or water. Through the presence of all these components in the food web, each species is held in check, and the community maintains its stability.

Reflecting on the Activity and the Challenge

In this activity you looked at how every organism is dependent on other organisms and how they are all held together by a food web. You can now begin to understand how the stability of any ecosystem depends on each one of its components. In the **Bio Talk** reading section you were also reintroduced to many terms that are used by ecologists. In discussing your environmental issue, you will be expected to use these terms correctly. You will probably also want to explain the importance of some of these terms in your booklet to educate the public.

How are primary consumers a benefit to plants?

Biology to Go

1. In what ways are living organisms affected by other living organisms?

2. What is the role of decomposers in a biological community?

3. What is the difference between a food chain and food web? Use an example to explain your answer.

4. a) Why are autotrophs called the producers in an ecosystem?

   b) Why are heterotrophs called consumers?

5. Are you a herbivore, carnivore, or omnivore? Explain your answer to show that you understand the meaning of each term.

6. Create a food web that includes you and at least five other organisms. Identify the decomposers, producers, and consumers as you diagram your food web.

7. In which ecosystem would the removal of an organism disrupt stability more, an Arctic ecosystem or a deciduous forest? Explain your answer.

Water makes up the largest part of the biosphere. Aquatic regions, both freshwater and marine, are home to many species of plants and animals. As you inquire further into aquatic food webs, you may be surprised at how many different types of aquatic ecosystems exist.

Inquiring Further

Aquatic food webs

Water covers over two-thirds of the surface of the Earth. Research and construct an aquatic food web. Identify the producers and consumers.

Activity 3

Energy Flow in Ecosystems

GOALS

In this activity you will:

- Infer the loss of energy in the form of heat from the human body.
- Relate the laws of thermodynamics to the transfer of energy in a food chain.
- Calculate the energy lost at a given level in a food web.
- Explain the significance of a pyramid of biomass, a pyramid of numbers, and a pyramid of energy.

What Do You Think?

Heat stroke is caused by a failure of the heat-regulating mechanisms of the body. It can be caused by heavy exercise combined with hot and humid conditions.

- Where does the heat in the body come from?

Write your answer to this question in your *Active Biology* log. Be prepared to discuss your ideas with your small group and other members of your class.

For You To Do

As you work through this activity, consider whether there is any relationship between events like heat stroke and the heat that is stored and lost at each link in a food web.

1. Read through the steps of the activity.

   a) What are you investigating in this activity?

   b) Predict what you think will happen to the water temperatures in the containers.

24

2. You can now follow the steps to conduct the experiment. Put 600 mL of water in each of three containers. The temperature of the water should be 10°C. You may have to add ice. Remove the ice when the temperature gets to 10°C.

3. Have one student put one hand into the water in container A. Have that student put the other hand into the water in container B. In container A, move the fingers rapidly in the water. Do not move the hand in container B. Keep one hand moving and the other hand still for five minutes.

4. Another student will hold a thermometer in the water in container A. Read the temperature once each minute for 5 minutes.

a) What is the purpose of stirring the water?

b) Record the temperatures in the chart.

Clean up any spilled water immediately.

Minutes	Temperature Container A (moving hand)	Temperature Container B (still hand)	Temperature Container C (no hand)
1			
2			
3			
4			
5			

a) Record the temperatures in a chart similar to the above.

5. A third student will hold a thermometer and read the temperatures in container B. Also, stir the water in this container using the stirring rod.

6. A fourth student will hold a thermometer in container C. Stir the water in this container. Read the temperature once each minute for five minutes.

a) Why did you have a container that you did not put your hand in?

Wash your hands after completing the activity.

Active Biology

b) Record the temperature readings in the chart.

7. Make a line graph of the temperature readings for the three containers. You will have three lines on the same graph.

   a) In container B, you held your hand in cold water without

moving it. What happened to the temperature? Does this data support your prediction?

b) In container A, you exercised your hand. How did the temperature of the water change? Do your data support your prediction?

BioTalk

Pyramids of Mass and Energy

One of the most important abiotic factors that affects relationships in a community is energy. Organisms in an ecosystem are tied together by the flow of energy from one organism to another. The food chain that exists when a herbivore eats a plant and a carnivore eats a herbivore depends on the energy entering the community in the form of sunlight. Without the Sun, there would be no green plants, no herbivores, and no carnivores. (There are a few ecosystems that get their energy from another source.)

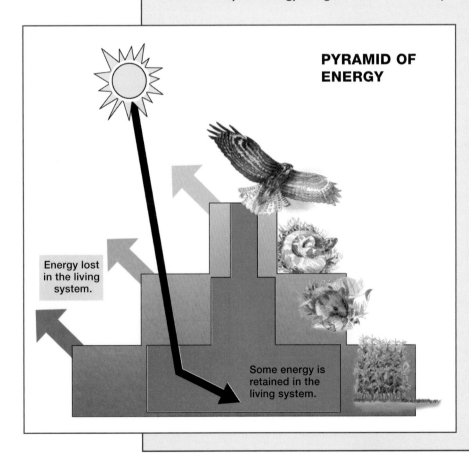

PYRAMID OF ENERGY

Energy lost in the living system.

Some energy is retained in the living system.

The size of a community, therefore, is limited by the amount of energy entering it through its producers. The total amount of chemical energy stored by photosynthesis is the gross primary productivity of the community. Much of that energy is used by the producers to grow and to maintain themselves. The remaining energy, which is available to the consumers as food, is the net primary productivity of the community.

The transfer of energy from producer to primary consumer to secondary consumer, and so on in a food web must follow the laws of **thermodynamics**.

The first law of thermodynamics states that although energy can be transformed, it cannot be created or destroy. Some energy from the Sun is transformed into a form that can be used by living organisms. However, if energy is not destroyed, what happens to it? Why is it necessary to keep adding energy in the form of sunlight? That is where the second law of thermodynamics comes into play. It states that in any energy transformation some energy is lost from the system in an unusable form.

Usually this is in the form of heat. In this activity, you actually measured the temperature increases that resulted from the heat loss from the human body. You noted that with exercise, the heat loss was even greater than without movement.

Among living beings, the transfer of energy in food from "eaten" to "eater" is really quite inefficient, and of course a great deal of the food does not get eaten at all. From grass to sheep the loss is about 90 percent.

It takes about 10 kg of organic matter in the grass to support one kilogram of sheep.

Bio Words

thermodynamics: the study of energy transformations described by laws

For the sake of simplification, assume that each consumer lives entirely on one kind of food. Then a person on a lake might live entirely on a given type of fish, for example. To support one kilogram of this person it takes about 10 kg of fish, 100 kg of minnows, 1000 kg of water fleas, and 10,000 kg of algae. This information in graph form is called a **pyramid of living matter**. Mass is a measure of the amount of matter in an object. Because much of the mass of living organisms is water, the producers first must be dried for a truer estimate of their mass when constructing a pyramid of matter. The pyramid shows that the amount of matter is greatest at the producer level.

It is possible to measure the amount of energy available at each level. The **pyramid of energy** that results from graphing these values also

THEORETICAL PYRAMID OF LIVING MATTER

human
100 kg

fish
1000 kg

minnows
10,000 kg

water fleas
100,000 kg

algae
1,000,000 kg

Humans have relied on fish as a source of food throughout history. Most of the fish protein was provided by species caught in the wild.

shows that the energy available is greatest at the producer level and steadily decreases at the other levels. Each step in the pyramid is called a **trophic level** (energy level). Because energy is lost at each transfer, the steps in a pyramid of energy are limited. Usually, there are no more than about five trophic levels in a food chain.

It is also possible to construct a pyramid of numbers by counting the number of organisms in a food chain. Although the largest number of organisms is usually found at the base of the pyramid, this is not always the case. For example, in a meadow there will be many more grass plants than there will be grasshoppers. However, a single tree can sustain many caterpillars.

Reflecting on the Activity and the Challenge

In this activity, you observed the loss of heat from the human body. You then related that to the loss of energy at each step of a food chain. You learned that the further you go up a food chain, the less energy is available. As part of your challenge you are expected to explain how energy flows through an ecosystem. You should also consider how the flow of energy is affected in the environmental issue that you have chosen.

Biology to Go

1. What is the relationship, if any, between the heat energy stored and dissipated at each link in a food web and the heat energy responsible for a heat stroke?

2. In the activity, the student who kept his/her hand in the water may have begun to shiver. Why do you suppose this happened?

3. Explain how the transfer of energy in a food chain follows the laws of thermodynamics.

4. Why is there a limit to the number of trophic levels in an energy pyramid?

5. Why is a pyramid of numbers not always a good example of the flow of energy through a food chain?

6. An energy pyramid illustrates the energy lost at each level of a food web. In general, each level of the pyramid has only 10% of the energy at the level below it. If the producer level (the lowest level) has 10,000 kilocalories available for the rest of the food web, how much energy is available for the other three levels?

7. An energy pyramid illustrates a great loss of energy as you go up the pyramid. When humans eat meat, they act as a top-level consumer. A steer eats a small amount of corn which contains 10 kilocalories. If you were to eat the same amount of corn you would get the same amount of energy from it as the steer. How much energy would you get from that small amount of corn if you ate some hamburger from that steer? Before you calculate this answer think about how this energy pyramid differs from the energy pyramid in the previous questions.

Inquiring Further

Biological amplification

What does biological amplification mean? Use the example of dichloro diphenyl trichloroethane, or DDT, to illustrate how biological amplification and food chains and energy pyramids are related.

The peregrine falcon is a bird of prey at the top of the food chain. As a result of biological amplification, falcons ingested high levels of the pesticide DDT. Falcons contaminated with DDT did not lay eggs or produced eggs with shells that broke.

Activity 4

Factors Affecting Population Size

GOALS

In this activity you will:

- Investigate the factors that affect the size of a population.
- Interpret a graph and make calculations to examine factors affecting fluctuations in populations.
- Calculate the doubling time of the human population.
- Distinguish between an open and closed population.

What Do You Think?

The population of your community may be going up, going down, or remaining the same. The change depends on whether individuals are being added to or taken away from your community.

- What can take place in your community, or any other community of living things, that can influence the size of the population?

Write your answer to this question in your *Active Biology* log. Be prepared to discuss your ideas with your small group and other members of your class.

For You To Do

This activity provides an opportunity for you to examine the factors that affect the changes (fluctuations) that occur in a population in an ecosystem.

Part A: Reindeer Population

1. In 1911, 25 reindeer, 4 males and 21 females, were introduced onto St. Paul Island near Alaska. On St. Paul Island there were no predators of the reindeer, and no hunting of the reindeer was allowed. Study the graph shown below and answer the questions in your *Active Biology* log.

a) In 1911 the population was 25 reindeer. What was the size of the population in 1920? What was the difference in the number of reindeer between 1911 and 1920? What was the average annual increase in the number of reindeer between 1911 and 1920?

b) What was the difference in population size between the years 1920 and 1930? What was the average annual increase in the number of reindeer in the years between 1920 and 1930?

c) What was the average annual increase in the number of reindeer in the years between 1930 and 1938?

d) During which of the three periods 1911—1920, 1920—1930, or 1930—1938, was the increase in the population of reindeer greatest?

e) What was the greatest number of reindeer found on St. Paul Island between 1910 and 1950? In what year did this occur?

f) In 1950, only eight reindeer were still alive. What is the average annual decrease in the number of reindeer in the years between 1938 and 1950?

2. In your group, discuss the questions on the next page. Then answer them in your *Active Biology* log.

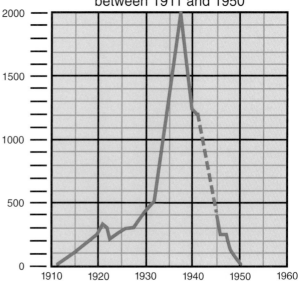

Changes in the
Reindeer Population on St. Paul Island
between 1911 and 1950

a) St. Paul Island is more than 323 km (200 miles) from the mainland. Could leaving or arriving at the island have played a major role in determining the size of the reindeer population? Explain your answer.

b) What might account for the tremendous increase in the population of reindeer between 1930 and 1938, as compared with the rate of growth during the first years the reindeer were on the island?

c) St. Paul Island is about 106 km^2 (41 square miles). What effect might 2000 reindeer have on the island and its vegetation?

d) Consider all the factors an organism requires to live. What might have happened on the island to cause the change in population size between 1938 and 1950?

e) Beginning in 1911, in which time spans did the reindeer population double? How many years did it take each of those doublings to occur? What happened to the doubling time between 1911 and 1938?

f) If some of the eight reindeer that were still alive in 1950 were males and some females, what do you predict would happen to the population in the next few years? Why?

g) What evidence is there that the carrying capacity (number of individuals in a population that the resources of a habitat can support) for reindeer on this island was exceeded?

h) What does this study tell you about unchecked population growth? What difference might hunters or predators have made?

Part B: Human Population

1. On a piece of graph paper, plot the growth of the human population using the following data.

Human Population Growth between A.D. 1 and 2000			
Date A.D.	Human Population (millions)	Date A.D.	Human Population (millions)
1	250	1930	2070
1000	280	1940	2300
1200	384	1950	2500
1500	427	1960	3000
1650	470	1970	3700
1750	694	1980	4450
1850	1100	1990	5300
1900	1600	2000	6080
1920	1800	2010	?

2. Use your graph to determine the doubling times for the human population between A.D. 1 and 2000.

   a) How much time elapsed before the human population of A.D. 1 doubled the first time?

   b) Is the amount of time needed for the human population to double increasing or decreasing?

   c) What does that indicate about how fast the human population is growing?

3. Extend your graph to the year 2010.

   a) What do you estimate the human population will be in that year?

4. Using the equations below, estimate the doubling time for the current population based on the rate of growth from 1990 to 2000.

   a) In what year will the present population double?

c) In what ways is the Earth as a whole similar to an island such as St. Paul? Does the Earth have a carrying capacity? Explain your answer.

$$\text{Annual rate of growth (in percent)} = \frac{(\text{population in 2000} - \text{population in 1990}) \times 100}{\text{population in 1990} \times \text{number of years}}$$

$$\text{Doubling time} = \frac{70}{\text{annual rate of growth}}$$

5. In your group, discuss the following questions. Then answer them in your *Active Biology* log.

   a) What similarities do you see between the graph of the reindeer population and your graph of the human population?

   b) What are the three or four most important factors required to sustain a population?

d) What might happen to the population of humans if the present growth rate continues?

e) What methods could be used to reduce the growth rate?

f) Suggest several problems in the United States that are related to the human population.

g) What are the most important three or four factors to think about with regard to the world population?

Bio Talk

CHANGING POPULATION SIZES

Four Rates Determine Population Size

The size of a population changes through time. Suppose a biologist counted 700 ponderosa pines on a hill in Colorado in 1990. In 2000, when the biologist counted the trees again, there were only 500. In other words, there were 200 fewer trees in 2000 than in 1990.

There are many reasons that a population of trees may decrease. These include forest fires and logging. What else may contribute to the decrease of population?

This is a decrease in the population of ponderosa pines. This change in population may be expressed as a rate. To find the rate you divide the amount of change by the amount of time for the change to take place. The rate is an average. In this example, the rate of change in the number of trees divided by the change in time may be expressed as: −200 trees ÷ 10 years = −20 trees per year. To the biologist, this means each year there were 20 fewer trees in the population. Keep in mind, however, that this rate is an average. It is unlikely the trees disappeared on a regular schedule. All of the trees may have been lost in one year due to a fire. Alternatively, selective cutting during several years may have caused the decrease.

→

35

Bio Words

death rate (mortality rate): the rate at which death decreases the size of a population

birthrate (natality): the rate at which reproduction increases the size of a population

immigration: the number of individuals of a species that move into an existing population

emigration: the number of individuals of a species that move out of an existing population

growth rate: the rate at which the size of a population increases as a result of death rate, birthrate, immigration, and emigration

What does the decrease of 200 pine trees in 10 years represent? Because pine trees cannot wander away, they must have died or have been cut down. In this situation, then, the decrease represents the **death rate**, or **mortality rate**, of the pine population. The number of deaths in the pine population per unit of time is the mortality rate. Mortality is not the only change that can affect a population, however. While some of the pines may have died, some young pine trees may have started to grow from seed. Death decreases a population; reproduction increases it. The rate at which reproduction increases the population is called the **birthrate**, or **natality.**

Organisms that can move have two other ways to bring about a change in population size. Suppose you were studying the pigeon population in your city or town. You might discover that a certain number of pigeons flew into the city in one year. This is called **immigration**. It occurs when one or more organisms move into an area where others of their type can be found. Immigration increases the population. While studying the pigeons, you might notice that a certain number flew out of the city. This is called **emigration**. It occurs when organisms leave the area. Emigration decreases the population. In any population that can move, then, natality and immigration increase the population. Mortality and emigration decrease the population. Thus, the size of any population is the result of the relationships among these rates.

The number of individuals of a species that move into and out of an area will affect the size of a population.

Natality, mortality, immigration, and emigration rates apply to every population, including the human population. The sum of these rates makes up the **growth rate** of a population. The growth rate of a population is the number of organisms added to (or subtracted from) a population in a year due to natural increase and net migration. Often, this rate is expressed as a percentage of the population at the beginning of the time period.

Population Density May Fluctuate

Any population has a built-in, characteristic growth rate. This is the rate at which the group would grow if food and space were unlimited and individuals bred freely. Environmental factors do affect a population's growth rate, however. The interaction of the population's natural growth rate and the environment determines the density of the surviving population. The maximum number of individuals that a given environment can support is called the **carrying capacity**.

Although there is variation among species, female ducks lay about 10 eggs per nesting attempt. The overall strategy for these birds is to get as many eggs out there as they can in the hopes that at least some will make it.

If you measure the density of a population at intervals during a given period of time, you seldom find any two consecutive measurements the same. Density increases or decreases continually. Most natural populations are **open populations**. These are populations in which individuals are free to emigrate or immigrate and in which the birth and death rates fluctuate. Variables in the environment, such as climate, available food, or the activities of natural enemies, are the causes of the fluctuations. In a closed population, birthrate and death rate are the only factors that affect the size of the population. The island of reindeer you studied in **Part A** is an example of a closed population.

Bio Words

carrying capacity: the maximum population that can be sustained by a given supply of resources

open population: a natural population in which all four factors that affect population size (death rate, birthrate, immigration, and emigration) are functioning

Active Biology

Active Biology A Vote for Ecology

Sometimes population fluctuations are fairly regular, and the peaks are at approximately equal time intervals. For example, populations of lemmings often peak every three or four years. Many of the animals that live in the northern parts of Europe, Asia, and North America show similar population cycles. Although the data show very regular cycles when they are plotted on a graph, the reasons for the seemingly regular cycles are not well understood. A combination of purely chance events also can produce apparently regular cycles.

Although populations may change cyclically, many population changes are permanent. If a population becomes extinct, for example, the change is permanent. Any permanent change in a population is a change in the community to which the population belongs. Permanent changes in one population also may affect other populations of organisms in the same community.

Lemmings are known for repeated population explosions. During the peak, the population may increase a thousand times. Food becomes scarce and lemmings must migrate to new areas.

Reflecting on the Activity and the Challenge

In this activity you discovered that birthrate, death rate, immigration, and emigration affect the growth rate of a natural, open population. Review the issue you have identified for research.

Consider if any of the factors involving population size are relevant to the issue. You will be asked to explain to the public the importance of these factors in providing the science behind your stand.

38

Active Biology

Biology to Go

1. How do each of the four limiting factors affect population growth?

2. Explain how limiting factors could play a role in the extinction of a population.

3. Distinguish between an open and closed ecosystem. Use examples to illustrate your answer.

4. Scientists studying an area of the tundra reported that they found 5 lemmings per hectare. They returned the following year and discovered that the density of the lemmings in the same area were 20 per hectare. What is the rate of growth of lemmings in the area, expressed as a percentage?

5. According to the U.S. Census Bureau, the population of the United States is influenced by the following:

   1 birth every 8 s;

   1 death every 13 s;

   1 immigrant every 22 s.

   Use these figures to determine the time, in seconds, it takes for the net gain of one person. (Hint: Start by calculating the number of births, deaths, and immigrants every minute. Round off to whole numbers.)

Inquiring Further

1. Population growth in different parts of the world

Research a place in the world where population growth is a problem today. How is it a problem? Research a place in the world where population growth is not a problem today. Why is it not a problem?

2. The truth behind lemming suicide

During the filming of the 1958 Disney nature documentary *White Wilderness*, the film crew induced lemmings into jumping off a cliff and into the "sea" in order to document their supposedly suicidal behavior. Research and report on the truth of this statement and the truth about lemming "suicide."

Activity 5   Competition Among Organisms

GOALS

In this activity you will:

- Observe the effects of competition among plants for space and nutrients.
- Describe the possible effects of introducing a nonnative species into an ecosystem.
- Explain why competition in nature is important.

What Do You Think?

Nature documentaries often feature the competition among animals for food, water, and space. These scenes are exciting to watch. However, plants seem to take a backstage to this type of activity.

- Do plants need to compete among themselves in any given environment?
- If plants do compete, how do they do it?

Write your answer to these questions in your *Active Biology* log. Be prepared to discuss your ideas with your small group and other members of your class.

For You To Do

This activity gives you an opportunity to observe the effect on plant growth when plants must compete for nutrients and space.

Part A: Competition among Plants

1. Fill five milk container bases with soil. Label the containers A through E.

2. Thoroughly moisten the soil in each container. Use the same amount of water to moisten the soil in each container.

   a) Why is it necessary to use the same amount of water in each container?

5. Place your containers in a low-light, room-temperature location (20°C is optimal). Keep the soil moist, but not soggy, by watering or misting every day or two.

6. When your plants sprout and begin to shed their hulls they are ready for light. Move them to a well-lighted location. If you go with sunlight be prepared to water more frequently. Room light will work as well and will not dry out the soil as quickly.

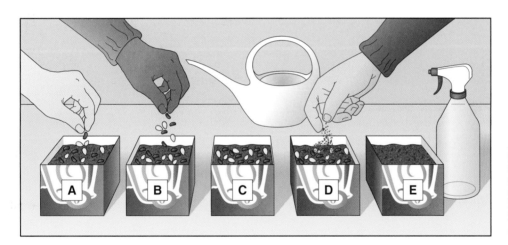

Do not eat any of the seeds in this activity. Wash your hands after handling the seeds and the soil.

3. Place seeds into the containers as follows:

   A. 5 crinkly cress (pepper grass) seeds
   B. 10 crinkly cress seeds
   C. 20 crinkly cress seeds
   D. 30 crinkly cress seeds
   E. 15 crinkly cress and 15 lettuce seeds.

   Spread seeds on the thoroughly moistened soil. (You are not expected to place them one at a time. Just spread them out as much as you can and as evenly as you can.)

4. Cover the seeds with a thin layer of soil.

   a) Count and record the number of seeds that germinated.

7. Keep the soil moist but not soggy by watering regularly. Water from the side if possible to prevent injuring the tiny plants. Again, make sure that each container is given the same amount of water.

8. Measure the heights of the plants and note the number and size of the leaves every two days for about three weeks.

   a) Record your observations.

   b) In which container were the cress plants the tallest?

c) In which container did the cress plants have the greatest number of leaves?

d) What happened to the appearance of the cress plants as the number of seeds in a container was increased?

e) Account for your observations when cress and lettuce seeds were planted together.

In the next part of this activity you will determine which plant species has an advantage under certain conditions. Each research group within the class can study a different set of variables.

Part B: Competition under Different Conditions

1. In this part of the activity you will once again use the bases of milk containers with moist potting soil to plant your seeds.

2. Plant seeds from various species according to the instructions on the packets. As a class, decide how you

will control the mix of seeds in each container.

3. Water each of the milk cartons with the same amount of water every second day.

a) Record the amount of water used.

4. Once seeds start to germinate, store each of the milk cartons in a different environment. You might want to use temperature, amount of light, or amount of water as variables. Measure the growth of each of the plants daily.

a) Does one type of plant begin to dominate the community? Is it the same type of plant in all containers?

b) Present your data and draw a conclusion.

c) Speculate about why one plant might be better adapted for a specific environment.

Do not eat any of the seeds in this activity. Wash your hands after handling the seeds and soil.

Bio Talk

Plants and Animals Compete for Resources

It is not uncommon for two organisms to compete with one another. Often, this happens when there is a limited supply of resources like water, food, sunlight, or space. If there are not enough resources to satisfy the needs of both organisms, they will compete with one another.

Sometimes this competition occurs between members of the same species. Male birds of the same species will battle each other fiercely for the ownership of a territory. The territory would allow sufficient food and habitat for the male and the female birds to make a nest, eggs, and feed offspring. Competition among individuals of the same species is a very important factor in evolutionary change.

Plants must deal with competition in different ways. Usually the plants that grow the tallest or establish the "best" root system are the survivors. In some cases, plants even secrete chemicals, which prevent the seeds from other plants from growing.

Competition may occur among members of different species. In this case, limited resources are usually the cause for competition.

Female eagles usually lay one to three eggs a few days apart. One to two days is a normal age difference between eaglets. Older hatchlings often dominate the younger ones for food. In a three-egg brood, the third chick has little chance of survival. A large number of adult eagles are non-breeders, probably due to competition within the species and variable annual food supply.

Bio Words

nonnative (exotic, alien, introduced, or non-indigenous) species: any species, including its seeds, eggs, spores, or other biological material capable of propagating that species, that is not native to that ecosystem

invasive species: a nonnative species whose introduction does or is likely to cause economic or environmental harm or harm to human health

Purple loosestrife can produce up to 2.7 million seeds per plant yearly and spreads across approximately one million additional acres of wetlands each year.

Scientists have found that usually only one species survives in laboratory experiments studying this type of interaction. However, the real world is a much more complex situation. At times two competitive species can exist together. For example, both hawks and owls hunt mice. Hawks hunt by day and owls hunt by night.

Introducing Nonnative Species

Sometimes a new species that has not been there before is introduced into an ecosystem. This is called a **nonnative species**. (Other terms that you may hear used to refer to these organisms are **exotic**, **alien**, **introduced**, or **non-indigenous**.) The introduction can be either intentional or accidental. Introduction of a nonnative species can have negative effects on the ecosystem. When this happens the species is considered invasive. It can cause economic or environmental harm, or harm to human health. **Invasive species** can be plants, animals, and other organisms (e.g., microbes). All these terms are clearly defined by the U.S. government (Executive Order 13112).

Why is the government so concerned with invasive species? Why should the public be concerned? Most scientists believe that on a global basis, next to habitat destruction, the second greatest destroyers of biodiversity are invasive species. In some cases, the result is the extinction of an entire existing species.

Species have sometimes invaded new habitats naturally. However, human actions are the main means of invasive species introductions. When people settle far from home, they often bring with them familiar animals and plants. Other species, like rats, make the trip unintentionally. In their new habitat there may have fewer predators or diseases, so their populations grow out of control. Organisms that they might normally prey on may not have evolved defense mechanisms. Native species may not be able to compete successfully for space or food and so are often pushed to extinction. The spread of nonnative organisms destroys healthy, diverse ecosystems. It replaces them with biologically impoverished, homogeneous landscapes.

It is unfortunate, but increased travel and trade are providing many new opportunities for the spread of nonnative species. In addition to which, one important feature that makes a community susceptible to invasion by nonnative species is the level of human-induced disturbance. For example, nonnative birds such as European starlings and house sparrows do well in ecologically disrupted areas such as cities, suburbs, and farms.

One hundred house sparrows were introduced into Brooklyn in the 1850s. From this initial introduction, the species expanded throughout the eastern United States and Canada. House sparrows are closely tied to human activity. This sparrow is usually absent from extensive woodlands and forests and from grasslands and deserts.

Reflecting on the Activity and the Challenge

In this activity you looked at the competition among organisms. Sometimes this competition occurs among members of the same species. Other times it occurs among members of different species. Competition is not always bad. In fact, it plays an important role in evolutionary development. However, when a nonnative species is introduced into an ecosystem, the competition can have devastating results. Consider how your issue relates to the competition among organisms. Has the environmental issue that you are investigating for the **Chapter Challenge** been caused by competition?

Penguins breed in colonies and can be fiercely territorial. Since nearly all of Antarctica is covered in ice, competition for breeding space among penguins is great.

Biology to Go

1. Why does competition occur among organisms?

2. What would be an advantage to competition between organisms of the same species?

3. Why do new species that are introduced into an ecosystem often become invasive?

4. What type of evidence would you look for in a natural setting to indicate that there is competition taking place among the plants?

5. Europeans, and their descendants in North America, often describe humans as being at the center of change. Not only do humans cause environmental changes, they are also responsible for those changes. In this worldview, the ideal human acts as a steward or protector for an ecosystem. By contrast, First Nations peoples often describe humans as belonging to an ecosystem. In this worldview, the ideal human lives in harmony with the ecosystem. How would the two worldviews differ in describing what has happened to ecosystems in the United States over the last century?

Inquiring Further

1. Investigating allelopathy

The production and release of substances by a plant that are toxic to neighboring plants is called allelopathy. Familiarize yourself with an allelopathic species in your area. Design an experiment to test which part of the plant is most toxic. Be sure to have your teacher approve your procedure if you plan on carrying out your experiment.

2. Invasive species

Research an invasive species in your area. Report your findings to the class.

Allelopathy benefited the sunflower growing in the wild. It reduced competition for nutrients, water, and sunlight. However, allelopathy works against sunflower crops. Sunflower crops must be rotated to avoid buildup of the "poison" in the soil.

Activity 6   Succession in Communities

GOALS

In this activity you will:

- Investigate succession after a natural disaster.
- Distinguish between primary and secondary succession.
- Explain how human activities can lead to succession.

What Do You Think?

Following a forest fire, all that remains is a charred landscape. Yet, within a few weeks the ground begins to turn green as living organisms return.

- From where does this new life come?

- How long will it take for the forest to return to its original condition?

Write your answers to these questions in your *Active Biology* log. Be prepared to discuss your ideas with your small group and other members of your class.

For You To Do

This activity provides you with an opportunity to examine how "life re-establishes itself" after a devastating blow.

1. On August 27, 1883, two volcanoes located on a single island in the Indian Ocean erupted at the same time. The blast was so great that a hole about 250 m deep remained where the peak of the volcano had been. The eruption on the island of Krakatoa has been said to be the loudest noise ever heard on Earth. The blast was heard in Hawaii, several thousands of kilometers away. Hot cinders and lava covered the island. Before the eruption, Krakatoa had been covered with a tropical forest. The eruption completely destroyed life on Krakatoa and two other nearby islands.

2. Two months after the eruption, scientists visited the island of Krakatoa. They found it steaming from a recent rain that had fallen on the lava that was still hot. In some places, the volcanic ash was washing away. In other places the ash was still more than 60 m deep. No life was visible.

3. Scientists visited the island nine months after the explosion, and at later times, to record the living things on Krakatoa. Some of the data recorded is shown in the diagram on the next page. Look for some interesting patterns in the rebirth of life on the island of Krakatoa. Study the plant life. (Reports of the animal life are interesting but too limited to use.)

a) What happens to the number of kinds of plants as the years pass?

b) Is there a change in the number of kinds of plant life?

c) Do the numbers of some kinds of plants change more than the numbers of other kinds?

d) Where do you think these plants might have come from? What reason do you have for your belief?

e) How long a period was needed for the complete recovery of the forest growth?

f) Write a statement that will describe the kinds of changes that have taken place on the island since the eruption.

g) Compare the "rebirth" of plant life on the coastal areas with the rebirth of plant life in the inland areas. How would you explain the difference?

SUCCESSION ON KRAKATOA

COASTAL AREAS	INLAND AREAS

3/4 years since eruption

Only algae and one lone spider found... mostly bare lava.

No plant or animal types found. Ground completely bare.

3 years since eruption

Ground completely covered with grasses. Many ferns, and many tropical seashore plants found. Insects also found.

A few grasses, many ferns and insects found.

13 years since eruption

Completely covered with young coconut trees, horsetail trees, and sugar cane plants. Lizards as well as insects found.

Almost all covered with grasses, orchids, and some horsetail trees. Lizards and insects found.

23 years since eruption

Completely covered as before, but with a greater number of trees.

Completely covered now with grasses, orchids, and groves of horsetail and young coconut trees.

47 years since eruption

By now a dense forest covers the area. All the previously listed plants and animals are found in abundance.

Inland areas now support same amount of plants and animals as the coast.

Bio Talk

Succession

The destruction of a mature forest by a severe fire is a devastating scene. Yet, even this charred scene holds promise of new life. Within a few weeks the ground will slowly turn green as annual and perennial plants return. These plants can tolerate full sunlight and the resulting high soil temperatures. They take root, grow, and reproduce in a soil made fertile by the mineral content of the ash. Within two or three years shrubs and young trees are evident and growing rapidly.

Forest fires are one of the most destructive natural forces known. While sometimes caused by lightning, nine out of ten forest fires are caused by humans. Natural-occurring fires are vital in maintaining healthy ecosystems. However, human-caused fires have devastating effects on both wildlife and human lives.

A few years later, an untrained observer would probably never know that the area had once been burned out. Over the long term, the forest will again reach maturity. This pattern is not limited to forests. It occurs in many other environments. This process of re-growth follows an environmental change. It is called **succession**. It describes the gradual change in an area. The change takes place as the area develops toward a final stable community. In every case, the final community that can exist is determined by the abiotic factors of the area.

Bio Words

succession: the slow and orderly replacement of community replacement, one following the other

Bio Words

primary succession:
the occupation by plant life of an area previously not covered with vegetation

secondary succession:
the occupation by plant life of an area that was previously covered with vegetation and still has soil

There are two types of succession: primary and secondary succession. **Primary succession** occurs in an area where no other community existed before. For example, this could happen on land left behind by a receding glacier. It could also happen on a newly formed volcanic island. **Secondary succession** occurs following destruction of a community. The re-growth after a forest fire is an example of secondary succession. Since soil is already present, the long time needed for soil to form in primary succession is not necessary.

Primary succession occurs on rock left behind by retreating glaciers, and transforms it into a living community. The process must begin with organisms that form organic soil, the pioneers or soil builders. This soil will be necessary to provide for the next group of plants to succeed.

After a forest fire, a sequence of ecological responses begins. Amid the charred forest remains, a pioneer community is established.

Each community goes through a succession of plant and associated animal species. The first community to appear is the **pioneer community**. It includes plants that are able to tolerate sunlight and the resulting high temperatures. This development of vegetation sets up new ground-level conditions. Eventually, conditions become more favorable to other plants that cannot tolerate full sunlight. These plants tend to be taller than the pioneer plants. This process continues through several in-between communities called **seral stages**. The plants and animals and their wastes at each stage contribute to the community development until a final community is reached. This final community is the one that can continue to perpetuate itself. It is called the **climax community**. Generally, both the biomass and the nonliving organic matter increase during the stages of succession. They then level off when the climax community is reached. The climate plant and animal life (biota) vary greatly by area. The types depend upon the tempereture and rainfall patterns.

Bio Words

pioneer community:
the first species to appear during succession

seral stages:
the communities in between the pioneer and climax community during the stages of succession

climax community:
the final, quite stable community reached during the stages of succession

Reflecting on the Activity and the Challenge

In this activity you observed some of the changes that occur after a dramatic environmental change. Sometimes, human activities are responsible for the environmental changes. Consider how the issue that you are researching for the **Chapter Challenge** came about. Can secondary succession be part of the solution to the problem?

Is the succession that occurs after a volcanic eruption primary or secondary succession?

Active Biology

Biology to Go

1. What is succession?

2. Explain the difference between primary and secondary succession.

3. Which community would support the greatest number and diversity of organisms, the pioneer community or the intermediate stages? Explain your answer.

4. Explain how abiotic factors change within a community as a result of the succession of vegetation.

5. Give two examples of how human activities can lead to secondary succession.

Inquiring Further

1. Primary succession

How does life establish itself on a rock surface? Describe the stages of succession that must occur to "transform" rock into a climax community.

2. Hydrarch succession

Hydrarch succession is the name for primary succession in a new freshwater environment. What type of organisms constitute the pioneer, seral, and climax communities in the stages of succession in fresh water?

3. Succession and Mt. St. Helens

At 8:32 Sunday morning, May 18, 1980, Mount St. Helens in southwestern Washington state erupted. About 600 km² of forest was blown over or left dead and standing. The eruption lasted nine hours, but Mount St. Helens and the surrounding landscape were dramatically changed within moments. Scientists and visitors follow the changes in the landscape and the volcano. Surviving plants and animals rise out of the ash, colonizing plants catch hold of the earth, birds and animals find a niche in a different forest on the slopes of Mount St. Helens. Research the succession pattern on Mt. St. Helens.

Volcanoes provide a unique opportunity to study plant succession, animal behavior, evolutionary and geologic processes, and ecology. Understanding how natural systems respond to disturbances is essential in facing environmental challenges of the future.

Activity 7   The Water Cycle

GOALS

In this activity you will:

- Measure the amount of water transpired by a plant.
- Describe the processes that take place in the water cycle.
- Provide examples of how human activities can affect the water cycle.
- Model the effects of acid rain on an ecosystem.

What Do You Think?

According to William Shakespeare, Caesar used part of his last breath to utter the words "Et tu, Brute" (even you, Brutus). His last breath would have been partly made up of water.

- Is it possible that the molecules of water that Caesar exhaled many centuries ago, are still a part of today's environment?

- Is it possible that these molecules could become a part of you?

Write your answer to these questions in your *Active Biology* log. Be prepared to discuss your ideas with your small group and other members of your class.

For You To Do

Plants absorb water through their roots and return water to the atmosphere through the process of respiration. In this activity you will measure the amount of water transpired by a plant over a period of time.

1. You will first construct a very simple "meter" to measure the loss of water. Place the tip of a 0.1 mL pipette into a piece of plastic tubing about 40 cm long.

2. Submerge the tubing and the attached pipette under water in the sink or a tray. Fill both with water. Make sure that all the air is drawn out of the tube and pipette. Leave the assembly under water while doing the next step.

3. Choose a branch from a plant. Suggested plants include Coleus and Zebrina. Submerge the end of the branch under water and make a small, slanted cut. This step is very important to ensure that no air bubbles are introduced into the xylem cells and the water will flow easily. Do not get the leaves wet. If you do, dry them gently with a paper towel before you begin your experiment.

4. While the branch and tubing are still under water, push the freshly trimmed end of the branch into the open end of the plastic tube. The end

of the branch should be about 1.5— 2.0 cm in the tube. There should be a very tight fit between the stem of the branch and the tube.

5. Bend the tubing into a U shape, as shown in the diagram. Clamp the tubing with the branch and the pipette onto a ringstand.

6. Once the "meter" is set up, wait about five minutes to make sure the plant is transpiring. After this initial waiting period, read the water level at "0 minutes." Then read the water level in the pipette every three minutes for a total of 30 minutes.

   a) Record your observations in a table.

7. At the end of your experiment, cut the leaves off the plant stem. Find the area of the leaf surfaces. You can do this by arranging all the cut-off leaves on a grid. Trace the edge of the leaves on to the grid. Count all of the grids that are completely within the tracing and estimate the number of grids that lie partially within the tracing.

   a) Record the area of the leaves in square centimeters.

   b) Calculate the water loss per square centimeter of leaf surface. Divide the water loss at each reading by the leaf surface area you calculated.

   c) Calculate and record the average loss per square centimeter for the class.

   d) Graph the loss per square centimeter over time.

Be careful when cutting the plant. Cut away from yourself. Report any injuries.

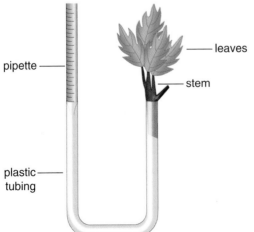

pipette —

— leaves

— stem

plastic — tubing

 Wash your hands after the activity.

e) Assuming that your plant stem continued transpiration at the same rate, estimate the total volume of water that might be transpired in 24 h.

8. Use the results of your experiment to answer the following questions.

a) List some of the factors that might affect the results of this experiment. Explain how each factor might affect your results.

b) How could you improve the design of the experiment to reduce errors?

c) Consider what factors could affect the rate of transpiration of a plant. Develop a hypothesis and design an investigation to test your hypothesis.

Bio Talk

The Water Cycle

Water is necessary to life in many ways. Land plants absorb water from the soil and land animals drink water or obtain it from their food. Water constantly bathes organisms that live in ponds, lakes, rivers, and the oceans. Other organisms rely on water to carry nutrients to their cells and organs. The cytoplasm in cells is mainly water.

Every day about 1200 km^3 of water evaporates from the ocean, land, plants, and ice caps. An equal amount of precipitation falls back on the Earth.

Bio Words

water (hydrologic) cycle: the cycle or network of pathways taken by water in all three of its forms (solid, liquid, and vapor) among the various places where is it temporarily stored on, below, and above the Earth's surface

evaporation: the process of changing from a liquid to a gas

condensation: the process of changing from a gas to a liquid

precipitation: water that falls to the Earth's surface from the atmosphere as liquid or solid material in the form of rain, snow, hail, or sleet

runoff: the part of the precipitation appearing in surface streams

groundwater: water contained in pore spaces in sediments and rocks beneath the Earth's surface

infiltration: the movement of water through pores or small openings into the soil and porous rock

aquifer: any body of sediment or rock that has sufficient size and sufficiently high porosity and permeability to provide an adequate supply of water from wells

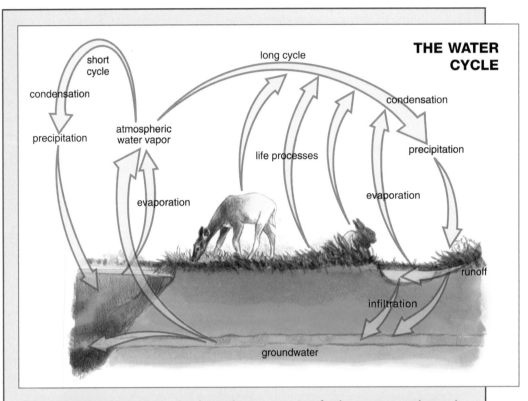

THE WATER CYCLE

The volume of water in the biosphere remains fairly constant through time. In fact, the water that you used today has been around for hundreds of millions of years. It has probably existed on the Earth's surface as a liquid, a solid, and a vapor. However, water is always moving from place to place. It is forever changing from one state to another. This complicated movement of the Earth's water is called the **water cycle** or **hydrologic cycle**. Some of the pathways of this cycle are shown in the diagram above.

One of the largest reserves of water on Earth is found in the oceans. The oceans contain about 97% of the Earth's water. Other surface water includes lakes, rivers, estuaries, marshes, and swamps. By contrast, the atmosphere holds less than 0.001% of the Earth's water. This means that rapid recycling of water must take place between the Earth's surface and the atmosphere.

By absorbing heat energy from the Sun, some of the water on the Earth's surface changes to water vapor by **evaporation**. It rises upward into the atmosphere until it reaches a point where the temperatures are low enough for the water vapor to condense to form tiny droplets of liquid water. This process is called **condensation**. These droplets of water are light. They collect around dust particles forming clouds or fog. They remain suspended in the atmosphere as clouds or fog and are supported by rising air currents and winds. When conditions are right, the droplets come together to form larger drops or sometimes ice crystals. Once the mass of the droplet or ice crystal can no longer be supported by air currents, **precipitation** occurs. Precipitation may take the form of rain, hail, sleet, or snow.

Snow falling high in the mountains or in the polar regions of the Earth may stay frozen there for years. Gradually, as layers of snow accumulate, the bottom layers of snow turn to ice, forming glaciers. Sometimes the snow or ice at the surface of the Earth can change directly back into water vapor. This process is called sublimation.

Other precipitation lands on the surface of the Earth and flows along the surface as **runoff**. The ground runoff gathers in streams, lakes, and oceans, and the cycle then repeats itself.

Approximately 1.7% of the water on Earth is stored in the polar icecaps, glaciers, and permanent snow.

However, some of the precipitation seeps into the Earth to form **groundwater**. This process is called **infiltration**. Sometimes the rock under the surface is very permeable. That is, water flows easily through it. In this case, some of the groundwater may seep to the surface, forming individual springs. **Aquifers** are large accumulations of underground water. They can provide an excellent source of water from wells. Groundwater

Active Biology

Bio Words

transpiration: the emission of water vapor from pores of plants as part of their life processes

flow, although measurable, is much slower than the flow in streams and rivers. That is because the passageways through the pore spaces in the materials beneath the Earth's surface are very small. Nonetheless, regardless of its speed, groundwater eventually also returns to the rivers, lakes, and oceans. And, the water cycle continues.

Plants and animals also play a very important role in the water cycle. Water enters living organisms by osmosis. However, through cellular respiration, water is released back into the atmosphere. As you saw in this activity, plants, especially broadleaf trees and shrubs play a major role in the water cycle through the process of **transpiration**. Transpiration is the loss of water through the leaves of a plant.

The Human Impact on the Water Cycle

The Earth's water supply remains constant, but humans can interfere with the water cycle. As population increases, living standards rise, and the industry and economy grow, humans place a greater demand on the supply of freshwater. The amount of freshwater needed increases dramatically, yet the supply of freshwater remains the same. As more water is withdrawn from rivers, lakes, and aquifers, local resources and future water supplies are threatened.

A person can probably exist on about 4 L (four liters is about one gallon) of water a day for drinking, cooking, and washing. At present in the United States, people use almost 6000 L a day for their needs and comforts. These include recreation, cooling, food production, and industrial supply.

A larger population and more industry also mean that

more wastewater is discharged. Domestic, agricultural, and industrial wastes include the use of pesticides, herbicides, and fertilizers. They can overload water supplies with hazardous chemicals and bacteria. Poor irrigation practices raise soil salinity and evaporation rates. Urbanization of forested areas results in increased drainage of an area as road drains, sewer systems, and paved land replace natural drainage patterns. All these factors put increased pressure on the water equation.

Pollutants that are discharged into the air can also affect the water cycle. Sulfur and nitrous oxides from the burning of fossil fuels, combustion in automobiles, and processing of nitrogen fertilizers enter the atmosphere. They combine with water droplets in the air to form acids. They then return to the surface of the Earth through the water cycle as acid precipitation.

Reflecting on the Activity and the Challenge

In this activity you observed one of the processes that take place in the water cycle. You learned that a great amount of water is transpired by a living plant. You also read about some of the other processes that are involved in the water cycle. The water cycle is very complex, and at any stage humans can have a significant impact. Perhaps the environmental issue you have chosen involves one part of the water cycle.

Biology to Go

1. Name and describe at least four processes that take place in the water cycle.

2. What is the energy source that drives the water cycle?

3. How has the water cycle determined partly where people live in the United States?

4. What would happen to the planet if the hydrologic cycle stopped functioning?

5. Describe three ways in which humans can have a negative effect on the water cycle.

Inquiring Further

Environmental models

Environmental models allow scientists to study what could happen to the plants and animals in an area if changes occurred. Models help check predictions without disrupting a large area.

Build an ecocolumn to research how acid rain affects an ecosystem.

(You will be allowed to use household vinegar as the acid.) An ecocolumn is an ecological model that is especially designed to cycle nutrients.

Record the procedure you will use. Have your teacher approve your procedure before you create your model.

ECOCOLUMN

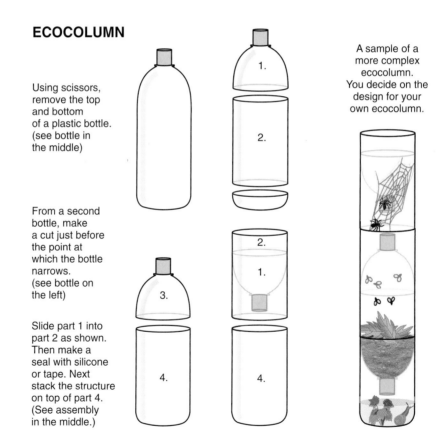

Using scissors, remove the top and bottom of a plastic bottle. (see bottle in the middle)

From a second bottle, make a cut just before the point at which the bottle narrows. (see bottle on the left)

Slide part 1 into part 2 as shown. Then make a seal with silicone or tape. Next stack the structure on top of part 4. (See assembly in the middle.)

A sample of a more complex ecocolumn. You decide on the design for your own ecocolumn.

Activity 8

Photosynthesis, Respiration, and the Carbon Cycle

GOALS

In this activity you will:

• Learn how oxygen cycles through photosynthesis and respiration.

• Practice safe laboratory techniques for using chemicals in a laboratory situation.

• Describe the cycling of carbon in an ecosystem.

• Speculate how human activities can affect the carbon cycle.

What Do You Think?

Consider the mass of a seed from a giant redwood tree and the tree itself. It is hard to believe that a giant of a tree began as a small seed.

• From where do the materials come to make up the mass of a mature tree?

Write your answer to this question in your *Active Biology* log. Be prepared to discuss your ideas with your small group and other members of your class.

For You To Do

In this activity you will investigate what happens when the exchange of carbon dioxide between a leaf and the atmosphere is blocked.

1. Three days before this activity, one plant was placed in the dark. A second plant of the same species was placed in sunlight.

63

a) Predict what you will find when you test a leaf from each plant for the presence of starch.

Day 1

Isopropyl alcohol is flammable and toxic. Do not expose the liquid or its vapors to heat or flame. Do not ingest; avoid skin/eye contact. In case of spills, flood the area with water and then call your teacher. Make sure you wear goggles, apron, and gloves

2. Remove one leaf from each plant. Use scissors to cut a small notch in the margin of the one placed in sunlight. Using forceps, drop the leaves into a beaker of hot (60°C) tap water.

3. When the leaves are limp, use forceps to transfer the leaves to a screw-cap jar about half full of isopropyl alcohol. Label the jar with your team symbol and store it overnight as directed by your teacher.

4. Select four similar leaves on the plant that has been kept in the dark, but do not remove them from the plant. Using a fingertip, apply a thin film of petroleum jelly to the upper surface of one leaf. Check to be sure the entire surface is covered. (A layer of petroleum jelly, although transparent, is a highly effective barrier across which many gases cannot pass.) Cut one notch in the leaf's margin.

5. Apply a thin film to the lower surface of a second leaf and cut two notches in its margin.

6. Apply a thin film to both upper and lower surfaces of a third leaf and cut three notches in its margin.

7. Do not apply petroleum jelly to the fourth leaf, but cut four notches in its margin; Place the plant in sunlight.

a) What is the purpose of the leaf marked with four notches?

8. Wash your hands thoroughly before leaving the laboratory.

Day 2

9. Obtain your jar of leaf-containing alcohol from Day 1. Using forceps, carefully remove the leaves from the alcohol and place them in a beaker of room-temperature water. (The alcohol extracts chlorophyll from the leaves but also removes most of the water, making them brittle.) Recap the jar of alcohol and return it to your teacher.

10. When the leaves have softened, place them in a screw-cap jar about half full of Lugol's iodine solution.

Lugol's iodine solution is used to test for the presence of small amounts of starch. Starch gives a blue-black color.

11. After several minutes, use forceps to remove both leaves, rinse them in a beaker of water, and spread them out in open Petri dishes of water placed on a sheet of white paper.

a) Record the color of each leaf. Recap the jar of Lugol's iodine solution and return it to your teacher.

b) What was the purpose of the iodine test on Day 2?

c) If you use these tests as an indication of photosynthetic activity, what are you assuming?

Lugol's iodine solution is poisonous if ingested, irritating to skin and eyes, and can stain clothing. Should a spill or splash occur, call your teacher immediately; flush the area with water for 15 minutes; rinse mouth with water.

12. Wash your hands thoroughly before leaving the laboratory.

Day 4

13. Remove from the plant the four notched leaves prepared on Day 1 and place them on paper towels. To remove the petroleum jelly, dip a swab applicator in the Histoclear™ and gently rub it over the surface of the film once or twice. Then gently use a paper towel to remove any residue of petroleum jelly. Discard the swab applicator and the paper towel in the waste bag.

14. Repeat **Steps 10** and **11.**

   a) Compare the color reactions of the four leaves and record your observations.

   b) In which of the leaves coated with petroleum jelly did photosynthetic activity appear to have been greatest? Least?

15. Wash your hands thoroughly before leaving the laboratory.

⚠ Histoclear is a combustible liquid. Do not expose to heat or flame. Do not ingest; avoid skin/eye contact. Should a spill or splash occur, call your teacher immediately; wash skin area with soap and water.

BioTalk

The Carbon Cycle

You take in carbon in all the foods you eat. You return carbon dioxide to the air every time you exhale. A plant also returns carbon dioxide to the air when it uses its own sugars as a source of energy. When another plant takes in the carbon dioxide during photosynthesis, the cycle of carbon through the community is complete. In this activity you observed what happens when this exchange of carbon dioxide does not take place. However, when the exchange does take place, the plant can use the carbon from the carbon dioxide to live and grow.

Carbon dioxide is also returned to the air by decomposers. When producers or consumers die, decomposers begin their work. As its source of energy, a decomposer uses the energy locked in the bodies of dead organisms. It uses the carbon from the bodies to build its own body. Carbon that is not used is returned to the air as carbon dioxide. Eventually, almost all the carbon that is taken in by plants during photosynthesis is returned to the air by the activity of decomposers.

Active Biology

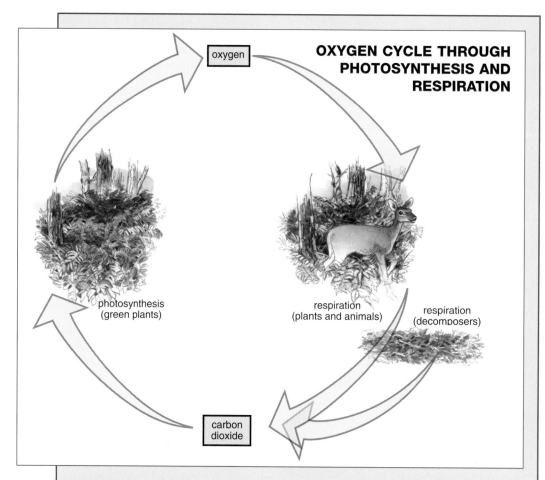

oxygen

OXYGEN CYCLE THROUGH PHOTOSYNTHESIS AND RESPIRATION

photosynthesis
(green plants)

respiration
(plants and animals)

respiration
(decomposers)

carbon
dioxide

Hundreds of millions of years ago, many energy-rich plant bodies were buried before decomposers could get to them. When that happened, the bodies slowly changed during long periods of time. They became a source of fuels like coal, oil, and natural gas. Today, when these fuels are burned, energy is released. The carbon in the fuels is returned to the air as carbon dioxide. You can see that even the energy obtained from fuels is a result of photosynthesis. The process in which carbon is passed from one organism to another, then to the abiotic community, and finally back to the plants is called the **carbon cycle**.

The Cycling of Matter

The energy from the Sun flows through the ecosystem in the form of carbon-carbon bonds in organic matter. When respiration occurs, the carbon-carbon bonds are broken and energy is released. The carbon is combined with oxygen to form carbon dioxide. The energy that is released is either used by the organism (to move, digest food, excrete wastes, etc.) or the energy may be lost as heat. In photosynthesis energy is used to combine the carbon molecules from the carbon dioxide, and oxygen is released. This is illustrated in the diagram. All the energy comes from the Sun. The ultimate fate of all energy in ecosystems is to be lost as heat. Energy does not recycle!

However, inorganic nutrients do recycle. They are inorganic because they do not contain carbon-carbon bonds. These inorganic nutrients include the phosphorous in your teeth, bones, and cell membranes. Also, nitrogen is found in your amino acids (the building blocks of protein). Iron is in your blood. These are just a few of the inorganic nutrients found in your body. Autotrophs obtain these inorganic nutrients from the inorganic nutrient pool. These nutrients can usually be found in the soil or water surrounding the plants or algae. These inorganic nutrients are then passed from organism to organism as one organism is consumed by another. Ultimately, all organisms die. They become detritus, food for the decomposers. At this stage, the last of the energy is extracted (and lost as heat). The inorganic nutrients are returned to the soil or water to be taken up again. The inorganic nutrients are recycled; the energy is not.

Bio Words

carbon cycle: the process in which carbon is passed from one organism to another, then to the abiotic community, and finally back to the plants

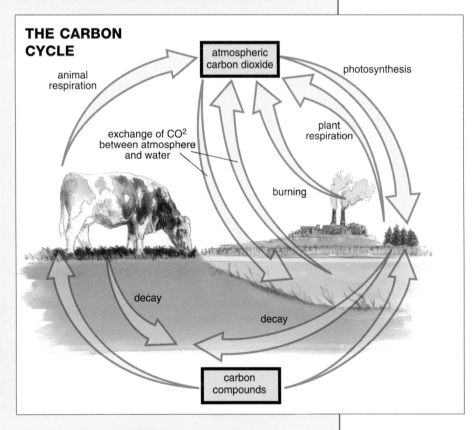

THE CARBON CYCLE

atmospheric carbon dioxide

animal respiration

photosynthesis

exchange of CO_2 between atmosphere and water

plant respiration

burning

decay

decay

carbon compounds

Reflecting on the Activity and the Challenge

In this activity you learned that carbon is the key element in all organic matter. You investigated the process of photosynthesis and then related this process to respiration in the carbon-oxygen cycle. The cycling of matter like carbon is essential to the survival of any ecosystem. You will need to explain this cycle in your booklet.

Biology to Go

1. Explain why photosynthesis and cellular respiration are considered to be paired processes.

2. What is the importance of decomposers in the carbon cycle?

3. What effect does the burning of fossil fuels have on the carbon cycle?

4. Scientists have expressed concerns about the burning of the rainforests to clear the land for the planting of crops.

   a) Explain how the burning of the forests could change oxygen levels.

   b) What impact would the change in oxygen levels have on living things?

Inquiring Further

The greenhouse effect

The term greenhouse effect was coined in the 1930s to describe the heat-blocking action of atmospheric gases. Research and report the connection between the greenhouse effect and the carbon cycle.

Activity 9   The Nitrogen and Phosphorous Cycles

GOALS

In this activity you will:

• Investigate the chemicals that promote and inhibit the growth of plant material.

• Explain the importance of nitrogen and phosphorous to organisms.

• Describe how nitrogen cycles in an ecosystem.

• Describe how phosphorous cycles in an ecosystem.

• Provide examples of how human activities can affect the nitrogen cycle.

What Do You Think?

Nitrogen is essential to all forms of life. Yet, recent studies have shown that excess nitrogen has been introduced into our ecosystems. It has had negative effects on the natural nitrogen cycle.

• What are the sources of the excess nitrogen?

• What are some of the negative effects of too much nitrogen?

Write your answer to these questions in your *Active Biology* log. Be prepared to discuss your ideas with your small group and other members of your class.

For You To Do

An excessive growth of algae (algal blooms) can make a lake very unappealing. More importantly, it places other organisms in the ecosystem in peril through lack of oxygen. In this activity you will investigate some of the chemicals that promote the growth of algae.

69

Handle all of the liquids and chemicals very carefully. They should all be considered contaminated and toxic. Keep hands away from eyes and mouth during the activity. Wash your hands well after the activity. Clean up any spills immediately.

1. Obtain three 1-L jars. Make sure the jars are rinsed thoroughly, so that there are no leftover traces of any chemicals, including soap. Fill each jar about three-fourths full with distilled water.

   a) Why is it important that the jars be cleaned before beginning this activity?

2. To each jar add a 10-mL sample of pond water. Stir the pond water thoroughly before taking the sample. The pond water will contain algae.

3. Label the jars A through C.

4. To each jar add the following:
   • To Jar A, add 15 gm of detergent.
   • To Jar B, add 15 gm of lawn fertilizer.
   • Do not add anything to Jar C.

   a) Many detergents contain phosphates. Fertilizers contain nitrogen and phosphates. Write as a question what you are investigating in this activity.

   b) What is the purpose of Jar C?

5. Cover each jar with plastic wrap so that dirt will not settle into the jar, but allow for some air to enter the jar.

6. Use a glass marker to mark the water level in each jar.

7. Set all the jars in a well-lighted place, but not in direct sunlight.

   a) Predict in which jar the algal growth will be the greatest? The least? Give reasons for your predictions.

8. Observe the jars each day for about two weeks. As water evaporates from the jars, add distilled water to bring the water back up to its original level. At the end of two weeks, you will pass the water in each jar through a separate filter.

   a) Record your observations every two or three days.

9. Find the mass of each of three pieces of filter paper.

   a) Record the mass of each in a table.

10. Fold the filter paper as shown and insert it into a funnel. Place the funnel in the mouth of another jar to collect the filtrate (the liquid that passes through the filter).

    Filter the liquid in each of the three jars.

11. Allow the filter papers and the algae residue to dry thoroughly.

    Find the mass of each piece of filter paper and algae. Calculate the mass of the algae.

    a) Record your findings in a table.

    b) Did your findings support your predictions? Explain any differences you found.

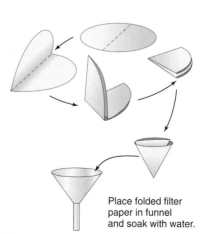

Place folded filter paper in funnel and soak with water.

Be very careful with the liquid and the algae residue. You should assume that disease organisms have grown in the water during the activity. Be very careful to avoid ingesting any of the water or residue. Dispose of all materials as directed by your teacher when finished.

Bio Talk

THE NITROGEN CYCLE

Nitrogen Fixation

Nitrogen is a basic building block of plant and animal proteins. It is a nutrient essential to all forms of life. Nitrogen is also required to make deoxyribonucleic acid or DNA. DNA is the hereditary material found in all living things. The movement of nitrogen through ecosystems, the soil, and the atmosphere is called the **nitrogen cycle**. Like carbon, nitrogen moves in a cycle through ecosystems. It passes through food chains and from living things to their environment and back again. Life depends on the cycling of nitrogen.

The largest single source of nitrogen is the atmosphere. It is made up of 78 percent of this colorless, odorless, nontoxic gas. With this much nitrogen available, you would think organisms would have no difficulty getting nitrogen. Unfortunately, this is not the case. Nitrogen gas is a very stable molecule. It reacts only under limited conditions. In order to be useful to organisms, nitrogen must be supplied in another form, the nitrate ion (NO_3-).

Bio Words

nitrogen cycle: the movement of nitrogen through ecosystems, the soil, and the atmosphere

nitrogen fixation: the process by which certain organisms produce nitrogen compounds from the gaseous nitrogen in the atmosphere

Three processes are responsible for most of the nitrogen fixation in the biosphere: atmospheric fixation by lightning, biological fixation by certain microbes, and industrial fixation. The enormous energy of lightning breaks nitrogen molecules apart. Only about five percent of the nitrates produced by nitrogen fixation are produced by lightning.

The nitrogen cycle is very complex. A simplified description is shown in the diagram on the next page. There are two ways in which atmospheric nitrogen can be converted into nitrates. The first method is lightning, and the second is bacteria in the soil. The process of converting nitrogen into nitrates is called **nitrogen fixation**.

A small amount of nitrogen is fixed into nitrates by lightning. The energy from lightning causes nitrogen gas to react with oxygen in the air, producing nitrates. The nitrates dissolve in rain, falling to Earth and forming surface water.

The nitrates enter the soil and then move into plants through their roots. Plant cells can use nitrates to make DNA, and they can convert nitrates into amino acids, which they then string together to make proteins. When a plant is consumed by an animal, the animal breaks down the plant proteins into amino acids. The animal can then use the amino acids to make the proteins it needs.

Some bacteria are capable of fixing nitrogen. These bacteria provide the vast majority of nitrates found in ecosystems. They are found mostly in soil, and in small lumps called nodules on the roots of legumes such as clover, soybeans, peas, and alfalfa. The bacteria provide the plant with a built-in supply of usable nitrogen, while the plant

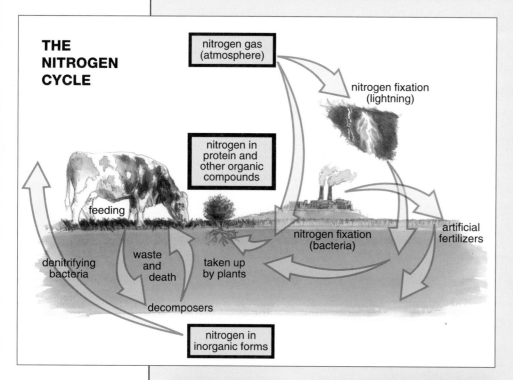

THE NITROGEN CYCLE

nitrogen gas (atmosphere)

nitrogen fixation (lightning)

nitrogen in protein and other organic compounds

feeding

artificial fertilizers

nitrogen fixation (bacteria)

denitrifying bacteria

waste and death

taken up by plants

decomposers

nitrogen in inorganic forms

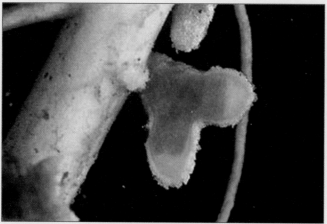

The most familiar examples of biotic nitrogen fixing are the root nodules of legumes, plants like peas, beans, and clover.

supplies the nitrogen-fixing bacteria with the sugar they need to make the nitrates. This plant-bacteria combination usually makes much more nitrate than the plant or bacteria need. The excess moves into the soil, providing a source of nitrogen for other plants. The traditional agricultural practices of rotating crops and mixed plantings of crops, one of which is always a legume, capitalizes on bacterial nitrogen fixation.

All organisms produce wastes and eventually die. When they do, decomposers break down the nitrogen-containing chemicals in the waste or body into simpler chemicals such as ammonia (NH_3). Other bacteria convert ammonia into nitrites, and still others convert the nitrites back to nitrates. These bacteria all require oxygen to function. The nitrates then continue the cycle when they are absorbed by plant roots and converted into cell proteins and DNA.

Farmers and gardeners who use manure and other decaying matter take advantage of the nitrogen cycle. Soil bacteria convert the decomposing protein in the manure into nitrates. Eventually, the nitrates are absorbed by plants.

Denitrification

At various stages in the decay process, denitrifying bacteria can break down nitrates to nitrites, and then nitrites to nitrogen gas. Eventually, the nitrogen gas is released back into the atmosphere. This process

A gardening magazine stated, "grass can actually poison itself as a result of the various chemical processes that occur in the individual grass plants if the grass roots do not have enough air." To what "poison" is the magazine referring?

Bio Words

denitrification: the conversion of nitrates and nitrites to nitrogen gas, which is released into the atmosphere

phosphorous cycle: the cycling of environmental phosphorous through a long-term cycle involving rocks on the Earth's crust, and through a shorter cycle involving living organisms

is called **denitrification**, and is carried out by bacteria that do not require oxygen. Denitrification ensures the balance between soil nitrates, nitrites, and atmospheric nitrogen, and completes the nitrogen cycle.

Older lawns often have many denitrifying bacteria. The fact that denitrifying bacteria grow best where there is no oxygen may help explain why people often aerate their lawns in early spring. By exposing the denitrifying bacteria to oxygen, the breakdown of nitrates to nitrogen gas is reduced. Nitrates will then remain in the soil, and can be used by the grass to make proteins.

THE PHOSPHOROUS CYCLE

The **phosphorous cycle** is different from the water, carbon, and nitrogen cycles because phosphorous is not found in the atmosphere. Phosphorous is a necessary element in DNA, in many molecules found in living cells, and in the bones of vertebrate animals. Phosphorous tends to cycle in two ways: a long-term cycle involving the rocks of the Earth's crust, and a short-term cycle involving living organisms.

In the long cycle living things divert phosphates from the normal rock cycle. Phosphorous is found in bedrock in the form of

THE PHOSPHOROUS CYCLE

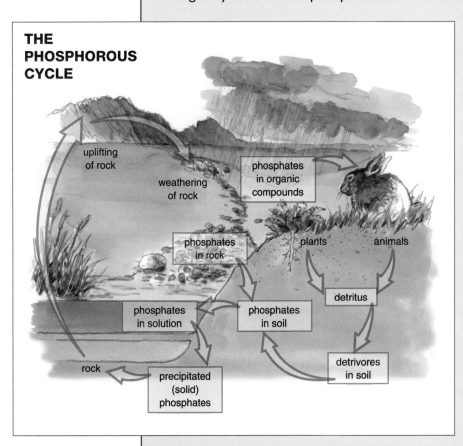

uplifting of rock

weathering of rock

phosphates in organic compounds

phosphates in rock

plants

animals

phosphates in solution

phosphates in soil

detritus

rock

precipitated (solid) phosphates

detrivores in soil

phosphate ions combined with a variety of elements. Phosphates are soluble in water and so can be drawn out of rock as part of the water cycle. Dissolved, phosphates can be absorbed by photosynthetic organisms and so pass into food chains. Phosphates eroded from rock are also carried by water from the land to rivers, and then to the oceans. In the ocean phosphates are absorbed by algae and other plants, where they can enter food chains. Animals use phosphates to make bones and shells. When they die, these hard remains form deposits on the ocean floor. Covered with sediment, the deposits eventually become rock, ready to be brought to the surface again. The cycle can take millions of years to complete. In the short cycle, wastes from living things are recycled by decomposers, which break down wastes and dead tissue and release the phosphates. The short cycle is much more rapid.

AGRICULTURE AND THE NITROGEN AND PHOSPHOROUS CYCLES

The seeds, leaves, flowers, and fruits of plants all contain valuable nutrients, which is why we eat them. However, as crops are harvested, the valuable nitrogen and phosphorous in these plant body parts are removed and do not return to the field or orchard they came from. This diversion of nitrates and phosphate from their cycles would soon deplete the soil unless the farmer replaced the missing nutrients. **Fertilizers** are materials used to restore nutrients and increase production from land. In this activity you investigated the effect fertilizer had on the growth of algae. Some estimates suggest that fertilizers containing nitrogen and phosphates can as much as double yields of cereal crops such as wheat and barley. However, fertilizers must be used responsibly. More is not necessarily better.

The accumulation of nitrogen and phosphate fertilizers produces an environmental problem. As spring runoff carries decaying plant matter and fertilizer-rich soil to streams and then lakes, the nutrients allow aquatic plants to grow more rapidly in what is called an algal bloom. When the plants die, bacteria use oxygen from the water to decompose them. Because decomposers flourish in an environment

Bio Words

fertilizer: a material used to provide or replace soil nutrients

Algae are generally thought of as simple, aquatic plants that do not have roots, stems, or leaves. A recurring problem in many bodies of water is algal bloom. An algal bloom is an abnormal increase of algae in a body of water. The most serious algal blooms are associated with human activities. Algal blooms deplete the water of oxygen and nutrients. In turn, this can kill other species in the water.

with such an abundant food source, oxygen levels in lakes drop quickly, so fish and other animals may begin to die. Dying animals can only make the problem worse, as decomposers begin to recycle the matter from the dead fish, allowing the populations of bacteria to grow even larger, and use still more oxygen.

Reflecting on the Activity and the Challenge

You have now investigated how several different types of matter cycle through ecosystems. You have also had an opportunity to learn about how humans can influence any one of these cycles. Consider how you will describe the importance of each of these cycles to the public. Also, consider whether or not the environmental issue that you have chosen deals specifically with one of these cycles. You will need to examine if any solution you provide will create a problem in any one of these cycles.

Biology to Go

1. Why is nitrogen important to organisms?

2. If plants cannot use the nitrogen in the atmosphere, how do they obtain the nitrogen they need?

3. How do animals obtain their usable nitrogen?

4. Explain why it is a good practice to aerate lawns.

5. Why is phosphorous important to living things?

6. With each harvest, nitrogen is removed from the soil. Farmers have traditionally rotated crops. Wheat, planted one year, is often followed by legumes planted the following year. Because the legumes contain nitrogen-fixing bacteria, nitrogen levels are replenished. The use of nitrogen-rich fertilizers has allowed farmers to not use crop rotation.

    a) What advantages are gained from planting wheat year after year?

    b) New strains of crops have been especially bred to take up high levels of nitrogen and harvests have increased dramatically. Speculate about some possible long-term disadvantages that these crops might present for ecosystems.

7. Before municipal sewers, the backyard outhouse was standard behind homes. They can still be found in some areas. To make an outhouse, a hole was dug in the ground to collect human wastes. Explain why the outhouse poses a risk to neighboring lakes, using information that you have gained about the nitrogen cycle.

Inquiring Further

1. The "new-tank syndrome"

Research to find out what is meant by the "new-tank" syndrome. How is it related to the nitrogen cycle?

2. Too much of a good thing

Which human activities impact on the nitrogen cycle? Choose one and explain how the impact of this activity on the environment could be reduced.

Biology at Work

Christy Todd Whitman

No person on the planet is more qualified to speak about the relationship between politics and environmental issues than Christy Todd Whitman. Whitman, 57, served as Governor of New Jersey from 1993 to 2000 and as the head of the Environmental Protection Agency from 2001 to 2003.

"Growing up on a farm I loved the outdoors. I loved to fish and swim and boat and bike and hike," Whitman says. "After seeing what happened as farms started to develop I got a real sense of the importance of protecting the environment."

Studying international government at Wheaton College in Massachusetts was also a natural extension of her curiosities as a child. "No matter what you're interested in—science or the arts or education—government impacts it in some way so I got interested in politics at an early age."

Whitman's work while EPA administrator forced her to deal with issues on a national level. She says that one of her biggest challenges was to educate the country–both individuals and corporate America–about the perils of ignoring the environment.

"A lot of the issues are very basic and we tried a lot of outreach programs. It's important to explain to people that everything you do has consequences, good and bad. For instance, we all live in a watershed so if you throw something out the window—a cigarette for example—that has an effect. If you change your oil in driveway or over-fertilize your lawn, it all will eventually wash down after a heavy rain. We found that every eight months there is as much oil deposited along the coastline from our everyday activities as was released for the Exxon Valdez spill. So what we're tying to get people to understand is that it

does matter what they do. Everything is cumulative."

And that includes big business. Although, Whitman is careful to point out that economic development does not have to be mutually exclusive to environmental protection.

"When you hear environmentalists yelling about business being bad for the planet or big corporations saying that they can't be profitable and environmentally conscious–you know that neither of those are true. You can have a cleaner, healthier environment, and a thriving economy. In fact, the environment needs the money produced by a healthy economy to invest in new technology. And there isn't a country in the world or a municipality or state in the world that is going to thrive economically if their environment is not good and healthy for the people who live there." Her solution? Incentives. The theory being that if you entice industries to develop environmentally sustainable practices, everybody wins.

Regardless of the fact that she is no longer head of the nations largest environmental group or governor of the 9th most populated state in the union, Whitman is still working to educate the public in an attempt to protect the planet's natural resources. "I am very proud of programs like Energy Star, which identifies energy efficient products such as washing machines, DVD players and other technologies to consumers," Whitman says. "In 2002, purchases from Energy Star saved consumers $7 billion and greenhouse gas emissions equivalent to the removal of 15 million cars from the road." And those are the kind of environmental impact numbers every politician would brag about.

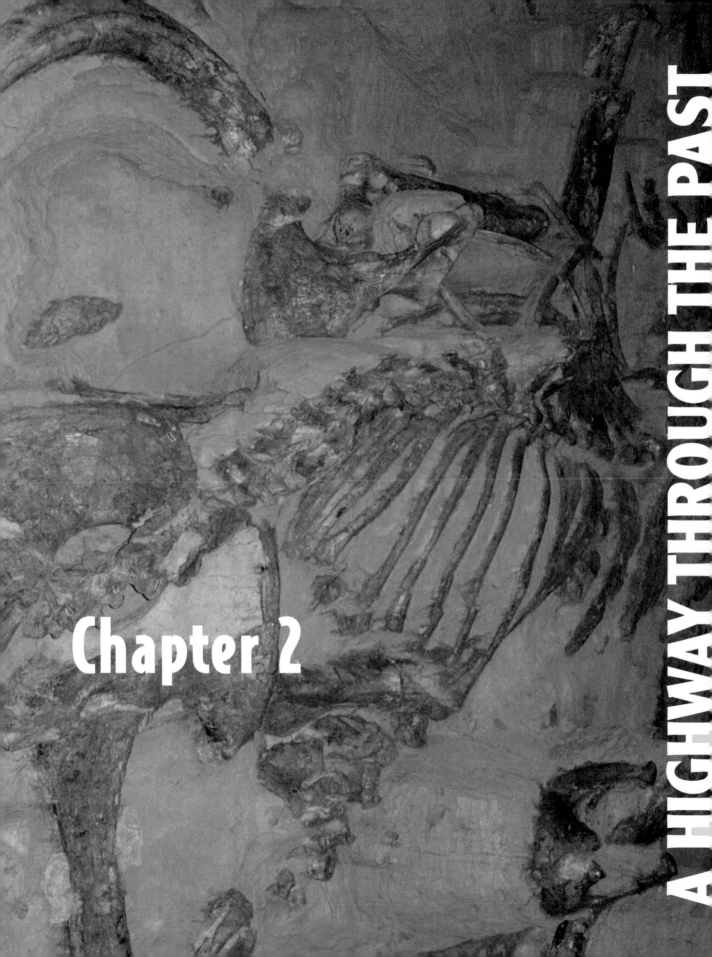

Chapter 2

2

A Highway Through The Past

Scenario

After much study, the State Department of Transportation decided that a stretch of road was needed to connect two very busy state highways. The study had included environmental assessment of the area that the road would be covering. Much to the frustration of the local people, this study had taken over a year to complete.

Now, by state law, before any road construction could begin paleontologists (scientists who study past life) from the state university had been given six months to study the land that would be covered by the new road. The local residents who would use this new road were very upset because of this further delay of six months. They were even more upset when they found out that the findings of the paleontologists would delay the road construction longer than six months, and maybe even indefinitely.

Chapter Challenge

The State Department of Transportation has concluded that in order to allow area residents a chance to express their views, a town-hall meeting should be held to discuss the issue. At this meeting, the paleontologists would also be given an opportunity to provide their findings and explain why they have asked for a delay or even an indefinite postponement of the construction. For your challenge, you may be asked to represent someone who is against building the road, someone who is for building the road, or one of the group of paleontologists. Or, you may be asked to represent a member of one of the levels of government involved in this project to explain why it is necessary to have all these studies

and subsequent delays. Your teacher will act as the chairperson. As you prepare for and participate in role-playing a town meeting, you will be expected to:

- explain why fossils are important;

- describe how the age of a fossil can be determined;

- indicate how a highway might impact on the natural-selection process of the living organisms in the area;

- explain why a great diversity of species is important for the survival of a community.

Criteria

How will your performance at the meeting be graded? Keep in mind that not everyone will be arguing every side of the issue. It is very important that you decide before the work begins how each person will be graded. Discuss this with your small group and then with your class. You may decide some or all of the following qualities are important:

- completeness and accuracy of the science principles presented in your side of the argument;

- accuracy of the science principles used to dispute your opponents' positions;

- forcefulness or conviction with which you present your argument;

- quality of questions you pose to the government officials.

Once you have determined the criteria that you wish to use, you will need to decide on how many points should be given to each criterion. Your teacher may wish to provide you with a sample rubric to help you get started.

Activity 1   Adaptations

GOALS

In this activity you will:

• Explain the meaning of adaptation.

• Speculate how adaptations help an organism survive in their environment.

• Distinguish between structural and behavioral adaptations.

What Do You Think?

Imagine surviving a temperature of −50°C and a blinding snowstorm. Imagine surviving a temperature of 50°C in an extremely dry landscape.

• How are plants and animals that live daily in these environments adapted for survival?

Write your answer to this question in your *Active Biology* log. Be prepared to discuss your ideas with your small group and other members of your class.

For You To Do

Part A: Observing Adaptations

An adaptation is an inherited trait or set of traits that improve the chances of survival and reproduction of organisms. In this part of the activity you will look at photographs of animals to observe and speculate about how the different types of adaptations help the organism survive.

1. Look closely at the following photographs. There is a living organism in each picture.

   a) Which organisms are exhibiting camouflage?

   b) How could this adaptation help an organism in capturing prey?

c) How could this adaptation help protect the organism from predators?

d) What other animals can you think of that use this type of adaptation for protection?

2. Some animals are not adapted to disappear into the background, but rather stand out.

Alligator.

Praying Mantis.

Snowshoe hare.

Chameleon.

Hawk moth.

Hawk-moth caterpillar.

Monarch butterfly.

Viceroy butterfly.

Look at the photographs of the hawk moth and caterpillar.

a) At first glance, of what animal does each remind you?

b) Why would birds avoid an animal with large eyes at the front?

c) What advantage does this adaptation present for the moth and caterpillar?

3. A monarch butterfly stores bad-tasting chemicals in its body that birds hate. The viceroy butterfly also has a bitter taste.

a) The monarch butterfly is brightly colored. Why do you think that this would be an advantage for the monarch butterfly?

b) Would the bright colors and bitter taste protect all monarch butterflies? Explain your answer.

c) Compare the appearance of the monarch and viceroy butterflies. Can you distinguish between them?

d) How would the viceroy butterfly's coloration be an advantage for its survival?

4. Adaptations are not limited to animals. Look closely at the plants or plant parts shown on the next page for their adaptations to the environment.

a) For each plant shown above, explain the adaptation(s) that you can see. Consider the environment in which the plants live, how they reproduce, and how they get their nutrients when identifying adaptations.

5. Not all adaptations need to be structural. Some adaptations can be behavioral.

a) How is each animal in the photographs adapted to a change in the environmental conditions from summer to winter?

b) How do other animals adapt to an environmental change? Give at least two examples.

c) What type of behavioral adaptation is the plant at right exhibiting?

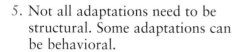

Active Biology

6. Invent an organism with specific adaptations. Consider one of the following:
   • camouflage
   • mimicry
   • warning coloration

Part B: How Well Adapted Are You?

In this part of the activity you will have an opportunity to examine one of your own adaptations that you probably take for granted.

1. Using masking tape, have your partner tape your thumb to your index finger on each hand. After your thumbs are securely taped, try each of the following activities. Rank the difficulty of each activity on a scale of 1 to 5.
   • picking up and carrying your textbook;
   • writing your name and address on a piece of paper;
   • picking up five coins from the floor and placing them in your pocket;
   • unbuttoning and buttoning a button;
   • tying up a shoe.

a) Did you find any of the activities impossible?

b) How did your ratings compare with others in your group and in your class?

c) Why do you think that an opposable thumb is an important adaptation for humans? (An opposable thumb is an arrangement in which the fleshy tip of the thumb can touch the fleshy tip of all the fingers.)

d) Do any other animals have opposable thumbs?

BioTalk

Adaptation

Diversity is a striking feature of living organisms. There are countless types of organisms on Earth. They are the result of repeated formation of new **species** and adaptation. There is a type of organism that can live in almost every type of environment on Earth. Living organisms are unique in their ability to adapt. The accumulation of characteristics that improve a species' ability to survive and reproduce is called **adaptation**. Adaptation occurs over long time periods. It is the environment that "selects" the best and most useful inherited variations. In this activity you observed just a few of the large number of adaptations that exist.

Bio Words

species: a group of organisms that can interbreed under natural conditions and produce fertile offspring

adaptation: an inherited trait or set of traits that improve the chance of survival and reproduction of an organism

Animals Adapt to the Demands of Their Environments

Animals cannot make their own food. Therefore, they must usually seek food. As a result, adaptations that allow animals to move are favorable. Movement is easier if the organism is elongated in the direction of movement. Fish, for example, are streamlined. This reduces water resistance as they swim. It is also easier to move if the sensory organs are concentrated in the head. The organs that detect food, light, and other stimuli should be in a position to meet the environment first. An organism can move more easily if it has a balanced body.

Animals have the type of body plan that is best suited to their lifestyle. The symmetry of an organism gives clues to its complexity and evolutionary development. Higher animals, including humans, are symmetrical along the mid-sagittal plane. This body plan is referred to as **bilateral symmetry**, in which the right and left halves of the organism are mirror images of each other. Some animals, however, are **radially symmetric**, or symmetric about a central axis.

How is body symmetry related to the speed at which an animal moves and to brain development? In general, animals that display radial symmetry are not highly adapted for movement. One explanation for the slower movement can be traced to the fact that no one region always leads. Only bilaterally symmetrical animals have a true head region. Because the head, or anterior region, always enters a new environment first, nerve cells tend to concentrate in this area. The concentration of

Bio Words

bilateral symmetry: a body plan that divides the body into symmetrical left and right halves

radial symmetry: a body plan that is symmetrical about a center axis

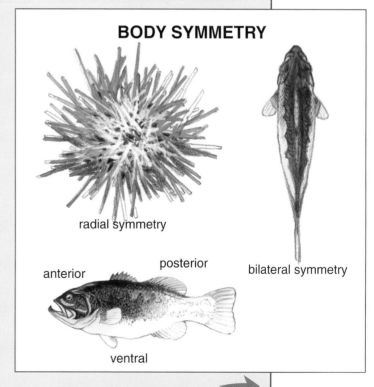

BODY SYMMETRY

radial symmetry

bilateral symmetry

anterior   posterior

ventral

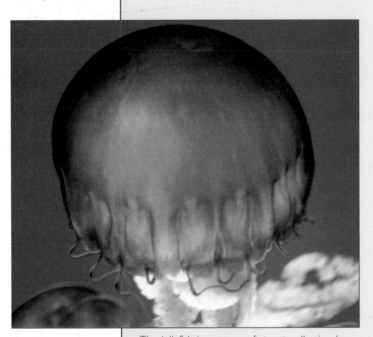

The jellyfish is a group of structurally simple marine organisms. The jellyfish has no head and a nervous system without a brain. The body exhibits radial symmetry.

nerve tissue at the anterior end of an animal's body, is an adaptation that enables the rapid processing of stimuli such as food or danger. Not surprisingly, the faster the animal moves, the more important is the immediate processing of environmental information. Every environment places special demands on the organisms living there. Seawater is fairly uniform. It poses the least stress for animal life. Oxygen is usually adequate. The temperatures and salt content are fairly constant. There is little danger that the organism will dry up. In contrast, the salt and oxygen contents of fresh water vary greatly.

Organisms that live in water have special adaptations. Gills, for example, allow the organisms to use the oxygen found in water. On land, oxygen is plentiful. However, the organisms that live there must protect themselves from the dangers of drying up. These dangers increase greatly because air temperatures change daily and seasonally. Air does not provide the same buoyancy as water. Therefore, large terrestrial, or land-dwelling, animals require good supportive structures. On the other hand, there is less resistance to movement in air than in water. Arms and legs, which would hinder an animal's movement in water, may help on land. Thus, long appendages specialized for locomotion have evolved in terrestrial animals.

Plant Adaptations

Plants lack the ability to move and must survive in the environment in which they are living. A plant must do more than simply survive and grow bigger. It must grow in such a way that it can take the best advantage of the light, water, and other conditions available to it.

Desert plants are an excellent example of adaptation to an environment. Some have a thick waxy coating to prevent them from drying out. Some have long vertical roots enabling a plant to reach water sources beneath the soil. Others develop shallow roots that extend horizontally. This maximizes water absorption at the surface. Many desert plants have small and narrow leaves. This decreases the heating from the Sun.

Even though plants are not able to move, they are still able to disperse. They produce seeds and fruits or other reproductive structures that may be distributed far from the parent plant.

Some plant adaptations are also behavioral. A vine spreads its leaves outward and receives as much light energy as possible. It sends its roots downward and receives more water. Tendrils of a vine touch an object and quickly coil it. This secures the vine in its upward growth. A vine would not live very long if it did not send its roots downward and its stem upward. The manner of plant growth is believed to be governed chiefly by hormones that are produced within the plant. The hormones are produced in response to conditions around the plant such as sunlight and gravity. Thus, the plant can fit itself to the environment in which it lives.

Some plants have even become adapted to feeding on animals. In this activity you looked at the Venus flytrap. Its leaves have been adapted to capture prey. These plants do photosynthesize. However, these plants live in bogs where there is very little nitrogen available. Therefore, they require the nutrients they receive from digesting their prey. Of course, the plant must therefore also be adapted to digest its prey with the secretion of chemicals.

Tendrils are modified stems or leaves that wrap around a support. They enable the plant to achieve fairly extensive horizontal and vertical spread without the use of much energy, since they don't have to support their own weight. Tendrils seem to respond to touch so if the stem or tendril touches an object, it wraps around it. This response is known as thigmotropism.

Active Biology

Reflecting on the Activity and the Challenge

In this activity you had an opportunity to look at adaptations of different organisms. You learned that every environment places various demands on the organisms living there. Organisms have developed special adaptations for living in any given environment. The animals and plants in the area of the highway construction have also adapted to their environment. In an environmental study scientists would have assessed the impact the highway would have had on the animals and plants. You may need to address this issue in the town-hall meeting if you are representing a government employee.

Biology to Go

1. Explain the term adaptation.

2. Distinguish between a structural and a behavioral adaptation.

3. a) How can an animal's structure help it survive in different environments? Give three examples.

   b) How can an animal's behavior help it survive in different environments? Give three examples.

4. Do all animals living in the same environment have similar adaptations? Explain your answer.

5. A cross section represents a cut through the middle of an animal's body. Below are cross sections through an earthworm, sand worm, and a primitive insect.

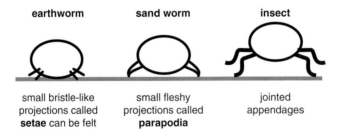

earthworm	sand worm	insect
small bristle-like projections called **setae** can be felt	small fleshy projections called **parapodia**	jointed appendages

   a) The jointed appendages of the insect lift the body from the ground. How does this help the insect move?

   b) What advantages might the fleshy projections of the sand worm have over the bristle-like projections of the earthworm?

   c) Predict which animal would be the fastest and give your reasons.

Inquiring Further

1. Animal adaptations to the arctic

Keeping warm is no easy task in the arctic where frigid weather lasts almost nine months of the year and where temperatures can plunge to −55°C. Even during the brief summer, when the land thaws and the Sun never sets, a sudden snowstorm can freeze everything. What adaptation have animals that live in this region developed?

2. Animal adaptations to the desert

Lack of water creates a survival problem for all desert organisms. However, animals have an additional problem. The biological processes of animal tissue can function only within a relatively narrow temperature range. Fortunately, most desert animals have evolved both behavioral and structural adaptations. Research the adaptations of animals living in desert regions.

Seals are well adapted to a cold environment. Their slick fur sheds water, and a thick layer of blubber beneath the skin keeps them warm in frigid temperatures.

The desert tortoise retreats to its burrow during the hottest times of the summer days. In the cold of winter it hibernates in its underground burrow.

Activity 2　　Is It Heredity or the Environment?

GOALS

In this activity you will:

• Observe how an inherited trait can be influenced by the environment.

• Distinguish between a genotype and a phenotype.

• Explain how the environment can influence the development of an inherited characteristic.

What Do You Think?

"You've got your mother's hair and your father's eyes." Almost everyone has heard about heredity at some point.

• How are personal characteristics passed on from one generation to the next?

• Can a personal characteristic be changed?

Write your answer to these questions in your *Active Biology* log. Be prepared to discuss your ideas with your small group and other members of your class.

For You To Do

In this activity you will use tobacco seeds from parents that carried the characteristics for albinism (no chlorophyll) but did not show it. Your observations will help you to understand that traits are inherited but are also influenced by the environment.

3. Cover two dishes with a lightproof container.

4. Leave the other two dishes exposed to the light.

5. Let the seeds germinate for about a week, adding a few drops of water to the paper every other day or whenever the paper begins to dry.

6. On the tenth day, begin to make entries in your table of results.

   a) Make up tables on which to record your results. You may wish to use tables similar to the ones shown on the next page.

   b) Every day, record how many and what kind of seedlings you observe.

7. When all or most of the seeds have germinated in the darkened dishes (probably the twelfth day) remove the covering. Place these dishes in the light next to the others.

   a) Continue to record the appearance of the seedlings through the thirteenth day.

8. Study all the data you have accumulated.

   a) Try to draw any conclusions that you can from your data.

9. Using your data for the seedlings that were kept in the light all the time, answer the following questions:

   a) How might you explain the differences you observed?

   b) Are these differences caused by heredity or environment?

1. Place blotting paper in the bottom of each of four Petri dishes. Moisten the paper, but be sure that it is not floating in water. Sprinkle about 40 tobacco seeds evenly over the surface of the paper. Keep the seeds a few seed lengths apart from each other.

2. Replace the covers of the dishes and place the dishes in a well-lighted place, but not in the direct sunlight. The temperature should be approximately 22°C.

 Wash your hands after handling the seeds. If mold forms in the dish, have your teacher dispose of the affected seeds.

Kinds of Leaves from Germinating Tobacco Leaves (Dishes Continuously Exposed to Light)			
	Albino	Green	Percentage of albino each day
10th day			
11th day			
12th day			
13th day			

Kinds of Leaves from Germinating Tobacco Leaves (Darkened Dishes)			
	Albino	Green	Percentage of albino each day
10th day			
11th day			

Kinds of Leaves from Germinating Tobacco Leaves (Covering Removed from Darkened Dishes)			
	Albino	Green	Percentage of albino each day
12th day			
13th day			

10. Consider the seedlings that were kept in darkened dishes.

   a) How do the percentages of albino and green seedlings compare with the percentages of albino and green seedlings that were continuously exposed to light?

   b) What is the environmental factor that is varied in this activity?

   c) Is this difference in percentages of seedlings kept in the light and seedlings kept in the dark due to inherited or environmental factors?

   d) What do you think is causing the differences in the appearance of the seedlings that were in darkened dishes?

11. Consider the seedlings that were first in darkened dishes and then exposed to light.

   a) How do the percentages of green and albino seedlings compare with the percentages of green and albino seedlings in the other situations?

   b) What happened to the appearance of many of the seedlings after the cover was removed?

   c) Does this support your answer to **Step 10 (d)**?

   d) What are the effects of light upon seedlings that carry a certain hereditary characteristic?

BioTalk

The Importance of Heredity and Environment

Why do offspring resemble their parents? Genetics, a branch of biology, tries to answer these types of questions about inheritance. Geneticists have found that most aspects of life have a hereditary basis. Many traits can appear in more than one form. A **trait** is some aspect of an organism that can be described or measured. For example, human beings may have blond, red, brown, or black hair. They may have tongues that they can roll or not roll. (Try it! Can you roll your tongue? Can your parents?) They may have earlobes that are attached or free. The passing of traits from parents to offspring is called **heredity**.

In *most* organisms, including humans, genetic information is transmitted from one generation to the next by deoxyribonucleic acid (DNA). DNA makes up the **genes** that transmit hereditary traits. Each gene in the body is a DNA section with a full set of instructions. These instructions guide the formation of a particular protein. The different proteins made by the genes direct a body's function and structure throughout life.

Chromosomes carry the genes. They provide the genetic link between generations. The number of chromosomes in a cell is characteristic of the species. Some have very few, whereas others may have more than a hundred. You inherit half of your chromosomes from your mother and the other half from your father. Therefore, your traits are a result of the interactions of the genes of both your parents.

Bio Words

trait: an aspect of an organism that can be described or measured

heredity: the passing of traits from parent to offspring

gene: a unit of instruction located on a chromosome that produces or influences a specific trait in the offspring

chromosome: threads of genetic material found in the nucleus of cells

Active Biology

Bio Words

dominant: used to describe the gene that determines the expression of a genetic trait; the trait shows up

recessive: used to describe the gene that is overruled by a dominant gene; the trait is masked

genotype: the genes of an individual

phenotype: the observable traits of an organism that result because of the interaction of genes and the environment

Gregor Mendel was the first person to trace the characteristics of successive generations of a living organism. He was an Augustinian monk who taught natural science to high school students. His origins were humble. However, his work was so brilliant that it took many years for the rest of the scientific community to catch up to it.

The modern science of genetics started with the work of Gregor Mendel. He found that certain factors in a plant cell determined the traits a plant would have. Thirty years after his discovery these factors were given the name genes. Of the traits that Mendel studied, he found that one factor, or gene, could mask the effect of another. This is the principle of dominance. He called the factor that showed up in the offspring **dominant**, and the factor that was masked **recessive**.

Genotype refers to the genes that an organism contains for a particular trait. The **phenotype** is the observable traits of an individual. Phenotype is a product of the interaction between the genotype and the environment.

All genes interact with the environment. Sometimes it is difficult to tell how much of a phenotype is determined by heredity and how much is influenced by the environment. A familiar example of how the environment affects the phenotype is the coloring of Siamese cats. The cats have a genotype for dark fur. However, the special proteins (enzymes) that produce the dark color work best at low temperatures. That is why Siamese cats have dark markings on their ears, nose, paws, and tail. These are all areas that have a low body temperature. Suppose a Siamese cat's tail were shaved and then kept at a higher than normal temperature. It would soon be covered with light-colored fur. However, these changes are temporary and only present if the environmental conditions are met. There are other examples of the influence of the environment on a phenotype. For a fair-skinned person, exposure to sunlight may produce hair that has lightened and a face full of freckles. Primrose plants are red if they are raised at room temperature, but white if they are raised at temperatures about 30°C. Himalayan rabbits are black when raised at low temperatures and white when raised at high temperatures.

The Siamese is a cat in which color is restricted to the points, i.e., nose, ears, legs, and tail. This is known as the Himalayan pattern. This coloration is a result of both hereditary and environmental factors.

Reflecting on the Activity and the Challenge

In this activity you saw that both heredity and environment contribute to the expression of a trait in a plant. You then read about how this also applies to animals. When thinking about how organisms are able to adapt, you must consider both inherited characteristics as well as the influence that the environment has on the organism. You will need to understand this for your **Chapter Challenge**. Also, in the next activity, you will investigate natural selection. Heredity and the environment both play a role in natural selection.

Biology to Go

1. Distinguish between a genotype and a phenotype.

2. What is the difference between a dominant and a recessive gene?

3. A dominant gene for a specific trait is inherited along with a non-dominant gene for the same trait. Which gene's "building instructions" will be used to assemble the specific protein?

4. In guinea pigs black coat is dominant to white. Is it possible for a black guinea pig to give birth to a white guinea pig? Explain your answer.

5. Explain how both heredity and environment contribute to the expression of a trait in plants.

6. Review your observations from the activity. Comment on the following statement: heredity can determine what an organism *may* become, not what it *will* become.

7. Can the environment change the development of an inherited characteristic? Use your observations from this activity to justify your answer.

Inquiring Further

1. Analyzing a genetic condition

What is a genetic condition? Choose a condition from one of the more well-known conditions, such as achondroplasia, cystic fibrosis, hemophilia, Huntington's chorea, Marfan syndrome, dwarfism, Down syndrome, Fragile-X syndrome, Tay-Sachs disease, sickle cell anemia, neurofibromatosis, etc. You may wish to investigate a condition with which you are personally familiar. Construct a hypothetical family tree to do a pedigree analysis of the condition. (A pedigree is used to trace inheritance of a trait over several generations.)

Down syndrome is caused by abnormal cell division in the egg, sperm, or fertilized egg. This results in an extra or irregular chromosome in some or all of the body's cells.

Activity 3   Natural Selection

GOALS

In this activity you will:

- Investigate the process of natural selection.
- Describe the major factors causing evolutionary change.
- Distinguish between the accommodation of an individual to its environment and gradual adaptation of a species.
- Read about the meaning of a theory in science.

What Do You Think?

One hundred rabbits were trapped and introduced to an island with a huge diversity of plants. The rabbits had several noticeable variations. Thirty years later scientists returned to the island. They were amazed that although the number of rabbits was still around 100, the later generations did not vary as much as the earlier rabbits had.

- What happened to the variations that were evident in the original species?

- How would you explain why the variations seemed to have disappeared?

Write your answer to these questions in your *Active Biology* log. Be prepared to discuss your ideas with your small group and other members of your class.

For You To Do

In this part of the activity you will study the process of natural selection. You will work with a hypothetical population of organisms in a hypothetical environment.

Active Biology

You will use a sheet of newspaper as the environment. You will use paper squares to represent individual prey. You will be given a chance to capture five prey individuals. The remaining prey will reproduce. You will then have another chance to capture the prey.

Part A: Predator and Prey

1. Work in groups of four. One student (the keeper) sets up the environment before each round (generation). The other three in the group act as "predators." They remove prey from the environment.

2. Lay a sheet of newspaper flat on a table or floor.

3. Take at least 50 each of newspaper, white, and red paper squares (150 squares). Keep the three types separate, as each represents a different type of the *same* prey species. Some are brightly colored. The others are not. An example of such different populations is the species *Canis familiaris*, the common dog. Although dogs come in many different colors and sizes, they all belong to the same species. The paper squares represent individuals of different colors, but of the same species.

4. The keeper collects 10 squares from each of the three prey populations. The keeper then mixes them and scatters them on the environment while the predators are not looking. Each predator may look at the environment *only* when it is her or his turn. When it is not your turn, simply close your eyes or turn your back until the keeper indicates that it is your turn. When it is your turn, remove five prey individuals as quickly as you can. Continue in order until each predator has removed five prey individuals.

5. Shake off the individuals left on the environment and count these survivors according to their type. They represent generation 1.

   a) Enter the data for your group in a table similar to the one shown.

   b) Place the data on the chalkboard also, so a class total can be reached.

Generation		Paper-Prey Species		
		Newspaper Individuals	White-Paper Individuals	Red-Paper Individuals
1	Team			
	Class			
2	Team			
	Class			
3	Team			
	Class			
4	Team			
	Class			

6. Analyze your data for the first generation. Record answers to the following questions in your *Active Biology* log:

a) Does any population have more survivors than the others?

b) Write a hypothesis that might explain this difference.

c) Consider your hypothesis. If it is valid, what do you predict will happen to the number of newspaper individuals by the end of the fourth generation? to the red-paper individuals? to the white-paper individuals?

7. The survivors will be allowed to "reproduce" before the next round begins. For each survivor, the keeper adds one individual of that same type. The next generation will then include survivors and offspring. This should bring the total prey number back up to 30.

8. The keeper scatters these 30 individuals on the habitat. Repeat the predation and reproduction procedures for three more generations.

a) Calculate the change in the number of all three populations after each round.

9. Look at your data and analyze your findings.

a) Does it take you a longer or shorter period of time to find one prey individual as you proceed through the generations? Give an explanation for this.

b) How does the appearance of the surviving individuals compare with the environment?

c) Is your hypothesis and your prediction in question supported, or do they need to be revised?

d) Were the red-paper individuals suited or unsuited for this environment? Explain.

e) Would you say this species *as a whole* is better adapted to its environment after several generations of selection by the predators? Explain.

10. Now think of the "real" world.

a) Is appearance the only characteristic that determines whether an individual plant or animal is suited to its environment? If so, explain. If not, give several other characteristics.

b) In your own words, what is natural selection? What role does reproduction play in your definition?

11. Now you may test some of your own ideas about natural selection.

• What would happen if there was a change in the environment, such as a change in color of the habitat?

• What would be the result if one type of paper square "reproduced" at a faster rate than the others?

Part B: Hypothetical Model

1. Examine the story shown in the pictures on the next two pages. It is purely a hypothetical model and not an actual situation that occurred.

2. Discuss the following questions in your small group. Then answer them in your *Active Biology* log.

a) What change took place in the environment of the original moth population?

b) What change was produced in the moth population as a result of this environmental change?

c) Provide evidence that indicates that the change in the moth population is not simply an

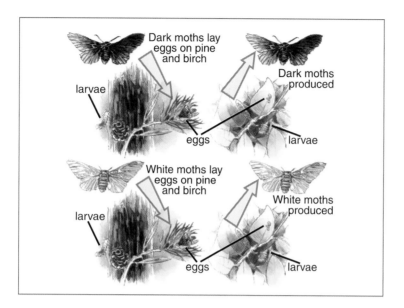

effect of the environment, but is really a hereditary population change.

d) Do you think that the change was a result of a change in reproductive capacity of the two kinds of moths? Do you think the change was a result of the survival of the moth best fit for the environment (selection pressure)?

e) What has happened to the frequency of the gene for speckled white color in the moth population now living in the pine woods?

f) What has happened to the frequency of the gene for speckled white color in the moth population living in the birch woods?

g) If environments change over a period of time, what must happen to populations if they are to survive?

h) If natural selection is responsible for the changes in frequency of black and of speckled-white moths in the two types of woods, what comparison can you make between the color of the favored type of moth and the color of the bark of the trees in each woods?

i) Assume there is benefit in protective coloration on the part of moths. What type of predators would you suspect to prey on moths?

j) What special abilities would these predators have to possess if they are really the agents of selection here?

k) Devise an experiment that would test this hypothesis.

Bio Talk

Theories in Science

Bio Words

theory: a proven and generally accepted truth

hypothesis: an idea that can be supported or not supported by observations and experiments

evolution: a gradual change in the characteristics of a population of organisms during successive generations, as a result of natural selection acting on genetic variation

The popular use and scientific use of the term "theory" are very different. Scientific theories attempt to provide explanations. Scientists make observations and then try to explain them. In popular terms you often hear the expression, "it's just a theory." That usually means that it is a guess. In scientific terms, a **theory** implies that an idea has been strongly supported by observations.

When scientists use the scientific method they often begin with questions from curious observations. They then develop hypotheses that can be tested experimentally. A **hypothesis** is a prediction between an independent (cause) variable and a dependent (result) variable. Hypotheses can either be supported or not, depending on the data collection. A hypothesis is not a guess. You developed and tested hypotheses in this activity. The hypothesis is then tested by further observations and experiments. Over time, if the observations and experiments satisfy the hypothesis, it becomes accepted as a scientific theory.

However, a theory is not the absolute truth. It only provides an explanation. The acceptance of a theory is often measured by its ability to enable scientists to make predictions or answer questions. A good theory provides an explanation that scientists can use to explain other observed events. Theories can be modified as new information becomes available or ideas change. Scientists continually "tinker" with a theory to make it more elegant and concise, or to make it more all encompassing.

Darwin's Hypothesis of Natural Selection

The theory of **evolution** owes much to the work of Charles Darwin. He presented his research in the mid-nineteenth century. However, Darwin never labeled his hypotheses as "evolution." He was interested in how species change and how new species come about. His many years of work led to explanations that have proved to be valid. But Darwin was not the first to think that existing species might evolve into new ones. However, Darwin was a most believable scientist for two reasons. First, he amassed a great deal of evidence. He verified its accuracy and presented it in a convincing way. Second, his hypothesis stated *how* change in organisms might take place, a contribution no one else had made.

From 1831 to 1836 Charles Darwin, a British naturalist, served aboard the H.M.S. Beagle on a science expedition around the world. The expedition visited places around the world, and Darwin studied plants and animals everywhere he went, collecting specimens for further study. In South America Darwin found fossils of extinct animals that were similar to modern species. On the Galapagos Islands in the Pacific Ocean he noticed many variations among plants and animals of the same general type as those in South America.

On November 24, 1859, the first edition of Darwin's *On the Origin of Species* was published. The book was so popular that its first printing was sold out in one day. There were, of course, many who disagreed with him. The theory of evolution has undergone many changes since Darwin's time. However, Darwin's original thinking still serves as a convenient introduction to the subject.

Here is his analysis:

• First, there are many differences among the individuals of every species. In a population, or group, of these individuals, variations occur. Usually it is safe to say that no two individuals are exactly alike. Darwin knew or suspected that many of the individual differences could be inherited.

• Second, the population size of all species tends to increase because of reproduction. One amoeba, for example, divides and produces two. These two divide, and the next generation numbers four. Then there will be 8, 16, 32, and so on.

• Third, this increase in the size of populations cannot go unchecked. If it did, the number of individuals of any species would outgrow the food supply and the available living space.

→

• Fourth, it is obvious that this huge increase seldom occurs in nature. The number of organisms in a species does not continue to increase over long periods of time. In fact, the sizes of many populations seem to remain nearly the same over time. How can this be explained? Observations of natural populations show that many individuals die before they are able to reproduce.

Why do some individuals die early, but not others? Darwin thought there must be a sort of "struggle for survival." The individuals of a species "compete" for food, light, water, places to live, and other things important for their survival. The "struggle" or "competition" may be either active or passive. That is, sometimes animals actually fight for food or the opportunity to mate. In other cases, there is no direct fight or competition. The first animal that happens to find a suitable living area may settle there. This prevents the area from being used by others. In either case, individuals with certain characteristics, or traits, will survive and produce offspring more often than individuals without them.

Consider, for example, how the African cheetah came to be such a fast runner. Cheetahs are hunters. They capture their food; mostly antelopes, gazelles, and birds, by first stalking near their prey. Then they run the prey down with a terrific burst of speed over a short distance. In any population of cheetahs, some can run faster than others. Those that run fastest are most successful in getting food. Those that are better at getting food also are more likely to survive.

While chasing prey, cheetahs often reach speeds of 70 miles per hour. Unfortunately, their great speed may not be enough for this species to survive. Scientists have found that wild cheetahs have virtually no genetic variation. Cheetahs suffer from inbreeding. This lowers their resistance to diseases and also causes infertility and high cub-death rates.

But survival is not the whole story. The characteristics that make an organism better able to survive in its environment are inherited. Therefore, those who survive are likely to pass on those characteristics to their offspring. For example, the surviving cheetah is likely to produce offspring with long, thin necks and powerful leg muscles, capable of great speed. Over many generations, then, one could expect an increase in the number of individuals that have these traits. The number with less beneficial characteristics would decrease. The organisms with the beneficial characteristics are likely to live longer and produce more offspring. Darwin called this process of survival and reproduction **natural selection**. Darwin thought that several factors were involved in natural selection:

1. The presence of variation among individuals in a population.

2. The hereditary basis of such variable characteristics.

3. The tendency of the size of populations to increase.

4. The "struggle for survival" (or competition for the needs of life).

5. A difference in the inherited characteristics that individuals pass on to succeeding generations.

Bio Words

natural selection: the differences in survival and reproduction among members of a population

Reflecting on the Activity and the Challenge

A change in the environment can have a large impact on the natural selection process. In this activity you investigated two situations. In the first, the "animals" that were best adapted to the environment were the ones to survive. In the second part you saw how a change in an environment could affect the natural selection process. Animals more suited to the changed environment would survive. You will need to explain the process of natural selection as part of your **Chapter Challenge**.

At one time some scientists believed that the necks of giraffes became long as a result of continually stretching to reach high foliage. Using what you know about natural selection, how would you explain the long necks?

Active Biology

Biology to Go

1. What evidence supports the following idea: hereditary differences are important in determining whether or not an individual survives and leaves offspring?

2. What is the difference between natural selection and evolution?

3. What did Darwin emphasize as the major factors in causing evolutionary changes?

4. What did Darwin mean by natural selection?

5. Write a short paragraph expressing your ideas now of what happened to the rabbit population on the island in the **What Do You Think?** section.

6. Comment on the validity of the following statement: Breeders of domestic stock abandon natural selection. Only artificial selection plays an important role in animal-breeding programs.

Inquiring Further

1. Animal-breeding programs

What are the advantages and disadvantages to animal-breeding programs? Research and report on the pros and cons of human intervention in genetic processes.

2. Captive breeding

Captive breeding is one strategy used by governments and non-government organizations to preserve rare and endangered species. What are the advantages and disadvantages of captive breeding?

Activity 4   The Fossil Record

GOALS

In this activity you will:

• Model ways in which fossils are formed.

• Explain the difference between a body fossil and a trace fossil.

• Describe the importance of fossils.

• Predict which animals are more likely to be found in the fossil record.

What Do You Think?

To hold a fossil in the palm of your hand is to have millions of years of history at your grasp. Fossils tell you about history, and like all good history, they help you to understand both the present and the past.

• What is a fossil?

Write your answer to this question in your *Active Biology* log. Be prepared to discuss your ideas with your small group and other members of your class.

For You To Do

In this activity you will have an opportunity to model different ways in which some fossils are formed. You will visit several stations.

Station 1: Preservation in Rock

You will mold a clamshell in plaster to model how it might be preserved in rock.

1. Obtain a large paper cup. Identify the cup with the name of your group. With a paper towel, smear petroleum jelly over the inside of the cup.

2. Mix plaster in another container following the directions on the package. Work quickly to complete the next four steps.

3. Fill the cup half full of plaster.

4. With the paper towel smear some petroleum jelly on both surfaces of a clamshell. Gently press the clamshell into the plaster.

5. Sprinkle a few pieces of confetti over the surface, enough to cover about 50% of the surface.

6. Fill the rest of the container with plaster.

7. Let the plaster harden overnight.

8. In the next class, remove the hardened plaster from the container. Set the plaster on its side and cover it with a towel. With a hammer gently hit the plaster to break it at the layer of confetti.

Wear goggles when using the hammer. Be sure others nearby are also wearing goggles. To contain any bits of plaster, cover the fossil model with cloth or paper before hitting it.

9. Observe your plaster molds and answer the following questions in your *Active Biology* log:

a) What does the plaster represent?

b) If you had never seen the clamshell, how would you figure out what the shell looked like by studying the fossil?

c) Clamshells have two parts to their shell. How many possible imprints could a clamshell form?

d) Why are fossils most often found in sedimentary rock formations?

Station 2: Preservation in Resin

You will encase a seed in glue to model how it might be preserved in a material like resin.

1. Obtain a small paper plate. Write your group's name on it. Use a paper towel to smear a small amount of petroleum jelly on a spot on the plate.

2. Using a hot-glue gun, put a bead of glue on the greased area of the plate.

3. Using tweezers, place the seed on the bead of glue. Add a few more drops of glue on top of the seed.

4. Let the glue harden overnight.

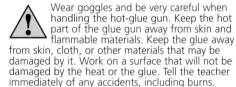

Wear goggles and be very careful when handling the hot-glue gun. Keep the hot part of the glue gun away from skin and flammable materials. Keep the glue away from skin, cloth, or other materials that may be damaged by it. Work on a surface that will not be damaged by the heat or the glue. Tell the teacher immediately of any accidents, including burns.

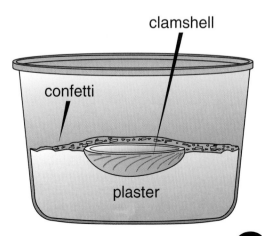

clamshell

confetti

plaster

5. In the next class, remove the bead of glue and observe. Answer the following questions in your *Active Biology* log:

a) Compare your preserved seed with a sample of amber provided by your teacher. How are they different? How are they similar?

b) Explain how a seed might end up being preserved in the resin.

c) Would you ever expect to see a large animal preserved in resin? Explain your answer.

d) Which type of fossil would be easier to identify: one preserved in rock, or one preserved in resin? Explain your answer.

Station 3: Preservation in Ice

You will freeze a small object in a cup of water to model how organisms can be preserved in ice.

1. Your teacher will provide you with a paper cup half full of water that is beginning to freeze. Put your group's name on the cup.

2. Gently push the object under the surface of the ice.

3. Add more water on top of the object.

4. Let the water freeze overnight.

5. In the next class, remove the ice from the paper cup. Answer the following questions in your *Active Biology* log:

   a) How do you think an organism could end up being preserved in ice?

   b) What type of organisms could be preserved in ice?

⚠️
Do not attempt to remove the object from the ice.

Station 4: Preserving Animal Traces

1. Flatten or roll out a piece of modeling clay to create a flat surface.

2. On the surface of the modeling clay, produce the pathway that an organism might leave in a muddy surface. Use your imagination to produce the pathway. You could represent anything from a worm crawling to a dinosaur trudging.

3. With a paper towel spread a small amount of petroleum jelly over the imprints you left in the modeling clay.

4. Mix plaster in a small plastic bag following the directions on the package. Cut the corner off the plastic bag. Squeeze enough plaster over the impression to fill the area.

5. Let the plaster dry overnight.

6. In the next class, remove the modeling clay from the plaster. Answer the following questions in your *Active Biology* log:

   a) In what kind of ancient environment(s) might you expect to have footprints formed?

   b) Once a set of fresh footprints have been made in the mud, what would have to happen to preserve them as rock?

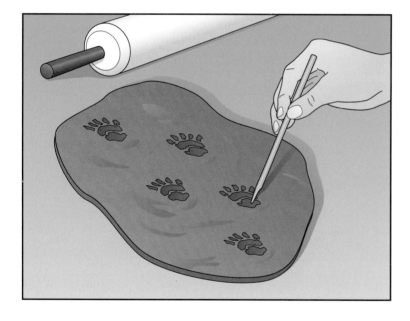

Bio Talk

THE NATURE OF THE FOSSIL RECORD

Making Models

Scientists often make models to help them understand how living things work. Models can be small-scale structures that simulate what is found in nature. For example, a scientist might reconstruct the climatic conditions of 65 million years ago to uncover what might have happened to the dinosaurs. Another type of model could be nonliving structures that work in a similar fashion. The human heart is often understood from the model of a pump. Recently, scientists have begun using computers to make mathematical models. Unlike the structural models, these models only exist as numbers. In this activity you modeled the formation of fossils.

The Importance of Fossils

What does the fossil record tell you? Among a number of things, it tells you that species are not unchangeable. The species you see around you today are not the ones that have always existed. Fossils provide direct evidence that organisms are continually evolving. However, it is important to note that evidence of evolution is very different from the theories of evolution, which you read about in the previous activity. Fossils tell you that life forms on Earth have changed. The theories attempt to explain how and why these changes took place.

Fossil Formation

Fossils are preserved evidence of ancient life. Some fossils are called **body fossils**. These are the preserved parts of plants and animals. Fossils may also be **trace fossils**. These fossils are traces of the activities of plants and animals, for example, tracks, trails, or scratch marks.

As you investigated in this activity, fossils form as a result of many processes. For example, most animals become fossilized by being buried in sediment. The sediments then accumulate and consolidate to form rock. Molds are fossils formed from the impressions in soft sediment of shells or leaves, for example, or from footprints or tracks. Casts are replicas formed when a hollow mold is subsequently filled with sediment—mud, sand, or minerals. Sometimes an insect might

Bio Words

fossil: any evidence of past life preserved in sediments or rocks

body fossil: a fossil that consists of the preserved body of an animal or plant or an imprint of the body

trace fossil: any evidence of the life activities of a plant or animal that lived in the geologic past (but not including the fossil organism itself)

→

become trapped in a sticky substance called resin, produced by some types of trees. The resin hardens to form amber. The insect fossil is preserved in amber, often perfectly. At other times natural mummies form when organisms are buried in areas like tar pits and peat bogs or dry environments like deserts or certain caves. Organisms buried in

Body fossil.

Trace fossil.

Cast.

glacial ice also can remain preserved for thousands of years. Finally, the cells and pore spaces of wood and bone can be preserved if filled with mineral deposits, a process called petrifaction.

Not all organisms become fossils. To begin with, very few escape the food chain. They are either eaten by other organisms or are broken down by decomposers. Soft body parts decay very quickly. You know from experience that it takes little time for meat and vegetables to spoil if left out of the refrigerator. More resistant parts, such as the exoskeletons of insects, vertebrate bones, wood, pollen, and

spores take much longer to decay. Thus, the likelihood of finding these in the fossil record is much greater.

The Fossil Record

Fossils typically form where sediments such as mud or sand accumulate and entomb organisms or their traces. The layers of hardened mud, sand, and other sedimentary materials are like a natural book of the Earth's history. Interpreting each layer is like reading the pages of a book. Unfortunately, there are many surfaces on the Earth where layers are not

Major Divisions of Geologic Time (boundaries in millions of years before present)			
Era	Period	Event	
Cenozoic	Quaternary	modern humans	
			1.8
	Tertiary	abundant mammals	
			65
Mesozoic	Cretaceous	flowering plants; dinosaur and ammonoid extinctions	
			145
	Jurassic	first birds and mammals; abundant dinosaurs	
			213
	Triassic	abundant coniferous trees	
			248
Paleozoic	Permian	extinction of trilobites and other marine animals	
			286
	Pennsylvanian	fern forests; abundant insects; first reptiles	
			325
	Mississippian	sharks; large primitive trees	
			360
	Devonian	amphibians and ammonoids	
			410
	Silurian	early plants and animals on land	
			440
	Ordovician	first fish	
			505
	Cambrian	abundant marine invertebrates; trilobites dominant	
			544
Proterozoic		primitive aquatic plants	
			2500
Archean		oldest fossils; bacteria and algae	

Active Biology

Bio Words

index fossil: a fossil of an organism that was widespread but lived for only a short interval of geological time

accumulating or where erosion is removing other layers. Thus, interpreting the layers is like reading a novel that is missing most of its pages. You can read the pages that are preserved and even group them into chapters, but much important information is missing from each chapter. Paleontologists (scientists who study fossils) use **index fossils**. These are fossils of organisms that were widespread but lived for only a short interval of geological time. They use index fossils to divide the fossil record into chapters. For example, dinosaurs are index fossils for the Mesozoic era, the unit of time that runs from roughly 245 million years ago (abbreviated Ma) to 65 Ma. In other

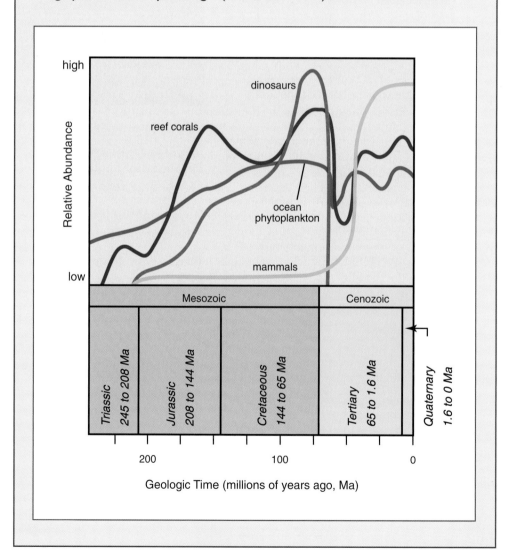

words, all dinosaur species evolved and became extinct during the Mesozoic era. Whales, horses, and many other mammal groups, on the other hand, are index fossils of the Cenozoic era, the unit of time that runs roughly from 65 Ma to the present. Using this and additional fossil evidence, paleontologists infer that the Mesozoic and Cenozoic eras represent two of the major chapters in the history of life.

The graph on the previous page summarizes the distribution of four groups of animals during the Mesozoic and Cenozoic eras. (Please note that this graph is not drawn to scale along the vertical axis; for example, the peak in dinosaur diversity is comparatively a small fraction of present day mammal diversity.) Although the graph is a rough summary of just a small part of the fossil record, paleontologists can get a much more accurate picture of life's history by examining specific pages in the record. You will do this in the next activity.

Reflecting on the Activity and the Challenge

In this activity you modeled some of the ways in which fossils can form. You also read about different types of fossils and the incomplete nature of the fossil record. You may have now developed a sense of the importance of fossils.

You can begin to appreciate what might be lost if fossil records were destroyed or disrupted. You will need to explain this at the town-hall meeting if you are representing one of the paleontologists.

Biology to Go

1. What is the difference between a body fossil and a trace fossil?

2. What are the chances of an organism becoming a fossil? Explain your answer.

3. a) What is an index fossil?

   b) How do paleontologists use index fossils?

4. Use evidence from this activity to explain how the biosphere and the geosphere are connected.

Inquiring Further

1. Carbon-14 dating

How is it possible to determine the age of organic matter using carbon-14? Research to find the physical and chemical principles on which this technique is based. What are the limitations of carbon-14 dating?

Activity 5   Mass Extinction and Fossil Records

GOALS

In this activity you will:

- Investigate fossil data for evidence of mass extinction and adaptive radiation.
- Explain the meaning of mass extinction and adaptive radiation.
- Describe the meaning of niche in an ecosystem.

What Do You Think?

Sixty-five million years ago the curtain came down on the age of dinosaurs when a catastrophic event led to their mass extinction.

- What type of disastrous event could have led to the extinction of such a large group of animals?
- Did any other life forms become extinct at this time in geological history?

Write your answer to these questions in your *Active Biology* log. Be prepared to discuss your ideas with your small group and other members of your class.

For You To Do

In this activity, you will investigate fossil data from those "pages" that represent the boundary between the Cretaceous and Tertiary periods (about sixty-five million years ago).

1. Your teacher will divide the class into groups of three or four students. With the other members of your group,

examine the six brachiopod fossils. Brachiopods are a group of marine animals.

a) What characteristics might paleontologists use to assign these fossils to different species?

b) What characteristics might paleontologists use to assign these fossils to one group?

2. Now examine **Graph A**. It plots the ranges of 50 different species of brachiopods across 15 m of sedimentary rock at one location in Denmark. This is one of the few places in the world that contains a continuous record of layers that represent the boundary between the

Cretaceous and Tertiary periods. Using a technique known as *magnetostratigraphy*, geologists infer that each meter of this sedimentary sequence represents 0.1 million years of history. The point "0 m" represents the boundary between the Cretaceous and Tertiary systems, 65 Ma (millions of years ago). Paleontologists sampled fossils from the locations shown along the left axis.

a) Which species became extinct at the Cretaceous-Tertiary (K-T) boundary?

b) Which species evolved after the K-T boundary?

c) Which species appear to have become extinct and then reappeared later?

d) What conclusions can you draw from this graph?

e) What are the limitations of the data shown in **Graph A**? (Hint: recall the processes by which fossils are preserved.)

⚠ Wash your hands after handling the fossils.

Graph A: Range of Different Species of Brachiopods

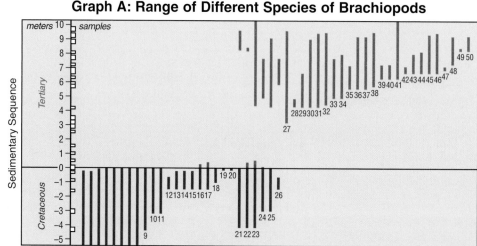

Graph B: Number of Families of Marine Organisms through Time

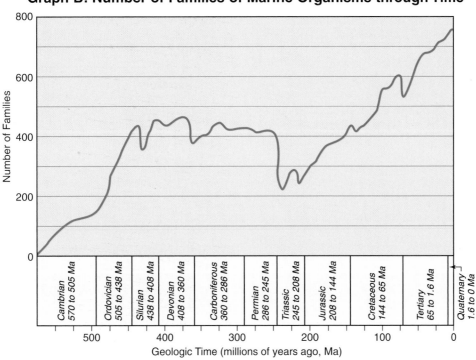

3. Paleontologists have compiled similar data on the ranges of existence of numerous other organisms during the Cretaceous and Tertiary periods. Examine **Graph B,** which shows a set of data assembled to illustrate the number of *families* (groups of closely related species) of marine animals through geological time.

   a) When was the number of families the greatest?

   b) Has the growth in the number of families been steady? Explain your answer.

   c) What do the dips in the graph represent?

   d) What inferences can you draw from this graph?

   e) What are the limitations of the graph shown in **Graph B**?

4. Now re-examine **Graph B**. Locate the times of the five greatest decreases in the number of families. Discuss why this might represent mass extinctions. Locate the times of the five greatest increases in the number of families. Discuss why this might represent adaptive radiations. (Adaptive radiation describes the rapid changes in a single or a few species to fill many empty functions in an ecosystem.)

   a) In your *Active Biology* log, construct a chart that summarizes your findings. Your chart should have two vertical columns, one labeled "Times of Mass Extinction" and the other labeled "Times of Adaptive Radiation." Fill in the chart with the estimated date that each event began and the name of the time period (e.g., "beginning of the Devonian period, roughly 410 Ma").

Graph C: Number of Families of Terrestrial Tetrapods through Time

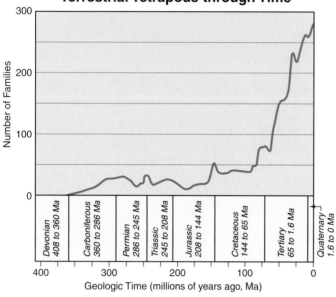

5. Now analyze **Graph C**, a graph constructed to show the number of families of terrestrial tetrapod families (land animals with four limbs) through geological time. Locate the greatest extinction events and adaptive radiations.

   a) Compare these events to the events listed in your chart for **Graph B**. Propose a hypothesis to account for the differences and similarities in these two graphs.

6. Consider the pattern of extinction and adaptive radiation in **Graph B** and **C**.

   a) How might adaptive radiation be related to mass extinctions? (Hint: consider how life on Earth might be different if dinosaurs still existed.)

Bio Talk

Making Inferences in Science

Have you ever wondered how scientists know so much about dinosaurs? No human ever saw a dinosaur eat or run. The huge lizards disappeared from Earth about 65 millions years ago. No fossil evidence of the human species, Homo sapiens, appears before 500,000 years ago.

The skeletons of dinosaurs have been reconstructed using fossil records. The skeletons provide indirect evidence of how the dinosaur might have lived. Evidence from the skull of a dinosaur may indicate that the dinosaur might have been a meat eater. The premise that this dinosaur killed other dinosaurs is called an inference. No one ever saw the dinosaur eating meat, the evidence to support this conclusion came from examining the skull shape and the structure of the teeth. Unlike a hypothesis, an inference cannot be tested.

Mass Extinction and Adaptive Radiation

Extinction is the total disappearance of a species. Extinction means that not a single organism of the species lives anywhere on Earth. The fossil record is a virtual graveyard of extinct species. It is strewn with the fossilized remains of millions of extinct species. David Raup, a paleontologist at the University of Chicago, notes that "only about one in a thousand species [that have lived on Earth] is still alive—a truly lousy survival record: 99.9 percent failure!"

Even more striking, however, is the fossil evidence of **mass extinctions**. These are episodes during which large numbers of species became extinct during short intervals of geological time. In geological time a few million years or less is a short period! The extinction of one species often has a domino effect. If one species vanishes, so do many others. Yet mass extinctions can present new opportunities to survivors.

Those best able to survive fill empty **niches**. (An ecological niche is the function a species plays in an ecosystem.) Plants and animals that have the greatest genetic variation are most often best able to fill these empty "spaces." This process is called **adaptive radiation**. In this activity, you investigated evidence of mass extinctions and adaptive radiations by analyzing data from the fossil record. Rapid evolution can also occur when a species moves into a new area. Natural variation within a species makes it easier for the species to adapt to different environments.

One remarkable mass extinction event occurred at the boundary between the Cretaceous and Tertiary periods, roughly 65 million years ago. This boundary separates the age of the reptiles and the age of the mammals. Geologists recognized this event over one hundred years ago when they realized that there was a striking change in the types of fossils deposited on either side of this boundary. This is where the language of science may become difficult to follow. However, no matter how it is said, the concepts are the same. This boundary ➔

Bio Words

extinction: the permanent disappearance of a species from Earth

mass extinction: the extinction of a large number of species during short intervals of geological time

niche: the ecological function of a species; the set of resources it consumes and habitats it occupies in an ecosystem

adaptive radiation: the diversification by natural selection, over evolutionary time, of a species or group of species into several different species that are typically adapted to different ecological niches

Model of a Brachiosaurus.

also separates two eras. These two eras are called the Mesozoic and Cenozoic. Dinosaurs were prevalent during the Mesozoic Era and extinct during the Cenozoic Era. The last segment of the Mesozoic Era is called the Cretaceous Period. The first segment of the Cenozoic Era is called the Tertiary Period. The abbreviation for the boundary between the Cretaceous and Tertiary periods is often referred to as the K-T boundary, where K is the abbreviation for the German form of the word Cretaceous. You may also hear of this time referred to the Mesozoic and Cenozoic boundary. No matter what you call it, there were dinosaurs before and there are no dinosaurs now, and it happened about 65 million years ago!

Moreover, at the end of the Cretaceous period virtually all plant and animal groups were lost from Earth, not just the dinosaurs. Yet, the beginning of the Tertiary period marks the start of the adaptive radiation of mammals.

The ultimate cause of the mass extinction at the Cretaceous/Tertiary boundary is still a debate among scientists. However, more and more evidence suggests that a meteorite impact caused the mass extinction. The impact of the meteorite created a chain of devastating environmental changes for living organisms.

Reflecting on the Activity and the Challenge

In this activity you had an opportunity to see that life forms that dominated the Earth many (geological) years ago are not here now. You also learned that the evidence to support this fact is found in fossil records. The new organisms that evolved to fill the ecological place of the extinct organisms are also part of fossil records. You probably have developed an even further appreciation of the importance of fossil records. You may wish to argue for a delay of construction of the new highway whether you represent the paleontologists or a concerned citizen.

Biology to Go

1. Explain the meaning of adaptive radiation in your own words.

2. What evidence do scientists use to support the idea of mass extinctions?

3. After a mass extinction, which organisms are most likely to survive? Explain your answer.

4. Explain why the extinction of one species can have a domino effect on an ecosystem.

Inquiring Further

1. The Cretaceous and Tertiary boundary event

Research the proposed causes of the mass extinction during this time period.

Provide at least two explanations. Which one do you think is more plausible?

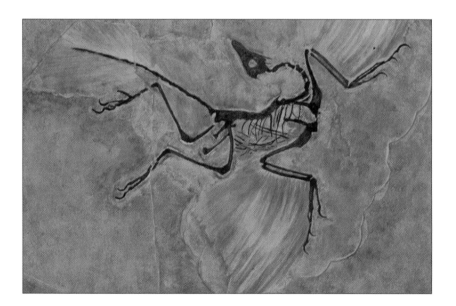

Active Biology

Biology at Work

Pat Holroyd

Paleontologist, University of California Berkeley Museum of Paleontology

Pat Holroyd examines a juvenile sea turtle skull, *Puppigerus camperi*.

"Believe it or not," says Pat Holroyd, "the science of paleontology owes a lot to the oil industry and construction projects in general." This statement may be surprising to you, coming from one of the best paleontologists in the world.

Holroyd's position at the University of California Berkeley Museum of Paleontology (UCBMP) has her in the field looking for rare fossils and overseeing construction projects as much as 12 weeks a year. "Under California law every construction project must produce an environmental impact statement before ever breaking ground," she explains, "and that must include a paleontology component. So, if someone wants to put in a transmission line or a road they must first look at how all the natural resources might be affected."

Yet, according to Holroyd, that rarely means development projects are blocked or even seriously delayed. "Mitigation is the word we like to use," she says. "When excavation begins, a paleontologist will be there to see if anything is coming out of the hole. What usually happens is that the paleontologist will jump in the hole and excavate for as long as she or he has to and then the project continues." As Holroyd explains, "Most important fossil finds do not happen despite development, but rather because of them. Most of the fossils we've found are only found because of construction projects. "The fact is that there are only a few thousand paleontologists in the entire world and they don't have the money to dig a 30-meter hole in the ground."

As a child, she loved playing in the dirt, but thought more about discovering pyramids than fossils. "It wasn't until college that I became interested in paleontology," Holroyd says. After graduating from the University of Kansas, she received a Ph.D. from Duke University in biological anthropology and anatomy. "I usually just say my degree is in paleontology," Holroyd laughs. During graduate school she worked with the U.S. Geological Survey in Denver and continued there for a year after graduation before moving over to UCBMP, where she's been happily digging in the dirt ever since.

In the larger sense, Holroyd's work is the study of small mammals and the effects of global warming. She and other scientists are actively trying to determine what a phenomenon like that does to a whole ecosystem, in an attempt to see what might be happening now. "If there is global warming now, then it's important to look at a period in the past when the globe went through similar changes," she explains. "Almost everything that we, as scientists, look at in terms of the impact humans are having or might have on the environment are things that we can find examples of in the fossil record."

126

Glossary

abiotic: the nonliving components of an ecosystem

adaptation: an inherited trait or set of traits that improve the chance of survival and reproduction of an organism

adaptive radiation: the diversification by natural selection, over evolutionary time, of a species or group of species into several different species that are typically adapted to different ecological niches

aquifer: any body of sediment or rock that has sufficient size and sufficiently high porosity and permeability to provide an adequate supply of water from wells

autotroph: an organism that is capable of obtaining its energy (food) directly from the physical environment

bilateral symmetry: a body plan that divides the body into symmetrical left and right halves

biodiversity: the sum of all the different types of organisms living on Earth

biosphere: the area on Earth where living organisms can be found

biotic: the living components of an ecosystem

birthrate (natality): the rate at which reproduction increases the size of a population

body fossil: a fossil that consists of the preserved body of an animal or plant or an imprint of the body

carbon cycle: the process in which carbon is passed from one organism to another, then to the abiotic community, and finally back to the plants

carnivore: an animal that feeds exclusively on other animals

carrying capacity: the maximum population that can be sustained by a given supply of resources

chromosome: threads of genetic material found in the nucleus of cells

climax community: the final, quite stable community reach during the stages of succession

community: all the populations of organisms occupying a given area

condensation: the process of changing from a gas to a liquid

consumer: a heterotrophic organism

death rate (mortality rate): the rate at which death decreases the size of a population

decomposers: organisms that break down the remains or wastes of other organisms to obtain their nutrients

denitrification: the conversion of nitrates and nitrites to nitrogen gas, which is released into the atmosphere

dominant: used to describe the gene that determines the expression of a genetic trait; the trait shows up even when the gene is present as a single copy

ecosystem: a community and the physical environment that it occupies

emigration: the number of individuals of a species that move out of an existing population

evaporation: the process of changing from a liquid to a gas

evolution: a gradual change in the characteristics of a population of organisms during successive generations, as a result of natural selection acting on genetic variation

extinction: the permanent disappearance of a species from Earth

fertilizer: a material used to provide or replace soil nutrients

food chain: a series of organisms through which food energy is passed in an ecosystem

food web: a complex relationship formed by interconnecting food chains in an ecosystem representing the transfer of energy through different levels

fossil: any evidence of past life preserved in sediments or rocks

gene: a unit of instruction located on a chromosome that produces or influences a specific trait in the offspring

genotype: the genes of an individual

groundwater: water contained in pore spaces in sediments and rocks beneath the Earth's surface

growth rate: the rate at which the size of a population increases as a result of death rate, birthrate, immigration, and emigration

herbivore: a heterotroph that feeds exclusively on plant materials

heredity: the passing of traits from parent to offspring

heterotroph: an organism that must obtain its energy from autotrophs or other heterotrophs

hypothesis: a statement that can be proved or disproved by experimental or observational evidence

immigration: the number of individuals of a species that move into an existing population

index fossil: a fossil of an organism that was widespread but lived for only a short interval of geological time

infiltration: the movement of water through pores or small openings into the soil and porous rock

invasive species: a nonnative species whose introduction does or is likely to cause economic or environmental harm or harm to human health

mass extinction: the extinction of a large number of species during short intervals of geological time

motile: having the ability to move spontaneously

natural selection: the differences in survival and reproduction among members of a population

niche: the ecological role of a species; the set of resources it consumes and habitats it occupies in an ecosystem

nitrogen cycle: the movement of nitrogen through ecosystems, the soil, and the atmosphere

nitrogen fixation: the process by which certain organisms produce nitrogen compounds from the gaseous nitrogen in the atmosphere

nonnative (exotic, alien, introduced, or non-indigenous) species: any species, including its seeds, eggs, spores, or other biological material capable of propagating that species, that is not native to that ecosystem

omnivores: a heterotroph that feeds on both plant materials and animals

open population: a natural population in which all four factors that affect population size (death rate, birthrate, immigration, and emigration) are functioning

organism: an individual living thing

phenotype: the observable traits of an organism that result because of the interaction of genes and the environment

phosphorous cycle: the cycling of environmental phosphorous through a long-term cycle involving rocks on the Earth's crust, and through a shorter cycle involving living organisms

pioneer community: the first species to appear during succession

population: a group of organisms of the same species occupying a given area

precipitation: water that falls to the Earth's surface from the atmosphere as liquid or solid material in the form of rain, snow, hail, or sleet

primary succession: the occupation by plant life of an area previously not covered with vegetation

producer: an organism that is capable of making its own food

pyramid of energy: a pyramid developed on the basis of the energy at each trophic level

pyramid of living matter: a pyramid developed on the basis of the mass of dry living matter at each trophic level

radial symmetry: a body plan that is symmetrical about a center axis

recessive: used to describe the gene that is overruled by a dominant gene; the trait is masked

runoff: the part of the precipitation appearing in surface streams

secondary succession: the occupation by plant life of an area that was previously covered with vegetation and still has soil

seral stages: the communities in between the pioneer and climax community during the stages of succession

sessile (non-motile): an organism that is permanently attached rather than free-moving

species: a group of organisms that can interbreed under natural conditions and produce fertile offspring

succession: the slow and orderly replacement of community replacement, one following the other

theory: a proven and generally accepted truth

thermodynamics: the study of energy transformations described by laws

trace fossil: any evidence of the life activities of a plant or animal that lived in the geologic past (but not including the fossil organism itself)

trait: an aspect of an organism that can be described or measured

transpiration: the emission of water vapor from pores of plants as part of their life processes

trophic level: the number of energy transfers an organism is from the original solar energy entering an ecosystem; the feeding level of one or more populations in a food web

water (hydrologic) cycle: the cycle or network of pathways taken by water in all three of its forms (solid, liquid, and vapor) among the various places where is it temporarily stored on, below, and above the Earth's surface

Spanish Glossary

abiótico (abiotic): los componentes sin vida de un ecosistema

acuífero (aquifer): cualquier cuerpo de sedimento o roca que tiene suficiente tamaño, nivel de porosidad y permeabilidad para permitir un suministro adecuado de agua de los pozos

adaptación (adaptation): un rasgo o conjunto de rasgos heredados que mejoran las posibilidades de supervivencia y reproducción de un organismo

agua subterránea (groundwater): agua que se encuentra en los poros de las rocas y el sedimento debajo de la superficie de la Tierra

autótrofo quimio-sintético (autotroph): un organismo que puede sintetizar su propia energía (alimento) directamente del ambiente físico

biodiversidad (biodiversity): la suma de todos los tipos diferentes de organismos vivos en la Tierra

biosfera (biosphere): el área en la Tierra donde se puede encontrar organismos vivos

biótico (biotic): los componentes vivos en un ecosistema

cadena alimenticia (food chain): una serie de organismos por los cuales pasa energía alimenticia en un ecosistema

capacidad de carga (carrying capacity): la población máxima que puede se sostenida por un suministro determinado de recursos

carnívoro (carnivore): un animal que se alimenta exclusivamente de otros animales

ciclo (hidrológico) del agua (water–hydrologic–cycle): el ciclo o la red de senderos tomados por el agua en todas sus formas (sólida, líquida y gaseosa) entre los varios lugares donde es guardada temporalmente en, bajo o sobre la superficie de la Tierra

ciclo de nitrógeno (nitrogen cycle): el movimiento del nitrógeno a través de los ecosistemas, el suelo y la atmósfera

ciclo del fósforo (phosphorous cycle): el ciclismo del fósforo ambiental a través de un ciclo a largo plazo envolviendo rocas en la corteza de la tierra y a través de un ciclo corto envolviendo organismos vivos

ciclo de carbono (carbon cycle): el proceso en el cual el carbono es pasado de un organismo a otro, de ahí a la comunidad abiótica y finalmente de vuelta a las plantas

comunidad (community): todas las poblaciones de organismos ocupando una área determinada

comunidad culminante (climax community): el final que una comunidad estable alcanza durante las etapas de sucesión

comunidad pionera (pioneer community): las primeras especies en aparecer durante la sucesión

condensación (condensation): el proceso de cambio de gas a líquido

consumidor (consumer): un organismo heterótrofo

cromosoma (chromosome): hilo de material genético encontrado en el núcleo de las células

desnitrificación (denitrification): la conversión de nitratos y nitritos a gas nitrógeno, el cual es liberado en la atmósfera

dominante (dominant): se usa para describir el gene que determina la expresión de un rasgo genético; el rasgo que se muestra

ecosistema (ecosystem): una comunidad y el medio ambiente físico que esta ocupa

emigración (emigration): el número de individuos en una especie que se muda fuera de una población existente

escurrimiento superficial (runoff): la parte de la precipitación que aparece en chorros superficiales

especies (species): un grupo de organismos que pueden ser reproducidos entre si bajo condiciones naturales y producir descendencia fértil

especies invasivas (invasive species): una especie que no es natural del área y que su introducción causa o puede causar daño económico, ambiental o a la salud humana

especies no naturales – exóticas, extranjeras, introducidas o no indígenas (nonnative - exotic, alien, introduced, or non-indigenous) species: cualquier especie, incluyendo sus semillas, huevos, esporas u otro material biológico capaz de propagar la especie y que no es natural de ese ecosistema

etapas serales (seral stages): las comunidades entre la comunidad pionera y la culminante durante las etapas de sucesión

evaporación (evaporation): el proceso de cambio de un líquido a un gas

evolución (evolution): cambio gradual en las características de una población de organismos durante generaciones sucesivas, como resultado de selección natural o variación genética

extinción (extinction): la desaparición permanente de una especie en la Tierra

extinción en masa (mass extinction): la extinción de un gran número de especies durante intervalos cortos en una era geológica

fenotipo (phenotype): los rasgos externos de un organismo que son el resultado de una interacción de los genes y el medio ambiente

fertilizador (fertilizer): un material usado para proveer o reemplazar nutrientes en el suelo

fijación del nitrógeno (nitrogen fixation): el proceso por el cual algunos organismos producen compuestos de nitrógeno del nitrógeno gaseoso en la atmósfera

fósil (fossil): cualquier evidencia de vida pasada preservada en sedimento o rocas

fósil de organismo (body fossil): un fósil que consiste del cuerpo preservado de un animal, planta o la impresión de un cuerpo

fósil índice (index fossil): el fósil de un organismo que se extendió pero vivió solamente por un corto intervalo de una era geológica

gene: una unidad de instrucción ubicada en un cromosoma que produce o influye un rasgo específico en la descendencia

genotipo (genotype): los genes de un individuo

herencia (heredity): el paso de rasgos de los padres a los descendientes

hervíboro (herbivore): un heterótrofo que se alimenta exclusivamente de plantas

heterótrofo (heterotroph): un organismo que debe obtener su energía de autótrofos u otros heterótrofos

hipótesis (hypothesis): proposición que puede ser probada o refutada por evidencia experimental o de observación

huella de fósil (trace fossil): cualquier evidencia de las actividades de vida de una planta o un animal que vivió en el pasado geológico (pero sin incluir el organismo fósil)

infiltración (infiltration): el movimiento del agua pasando por poros o pequeñas aberturas en el suelo o en roca porosa

inmigración (immigration): el número de individuos en una especie que se mueve adentro de una población ya existente

móvil (motile): tener la habilidad de moverse espontáneamente

nicho (niche): el rol ecológico de las especies; el conjunto de recursos que consume y los medios físicos ocupados en un ecosistema

nivel trófico (trophic level): el número de transferencias de energía un organismo tiene de la energía solar original que está entrando en un ecosistema; el nivel de alimentación de una o más poblaciones en una red alimenticia

omnívoro (omnivores): un heterótrofo que se alimenta tanto de plantas como de animales

organismo (organism): un ser vivo individual

organismos de descomposición (decomposers): organismos que descomponen los restos o desperdicios de otros organismos para obtener sus alimentos

pirámide de energía (pyramid of energy): una pirámide desarrollada basada en energía en cada nivel trófico

pirámide de material viviente (pyramid of living matter): una pirámide desarrollada basada en la masa de material viviente seca en cada nivel trófico

población (population): un grupo de organismos de la misma especie ocupando una área determinada

población abierta (open population): una población natural en la cual los cuatro factores que afectan el tamaño de la población (tasa de mortalidad, tasa de natalidad, inmigración y emigración) están en funcionamiento

precipitación (precipitation): agua que cae de la atmósfera sobre la superficie de la Tierra como material líquido o sólido en forma de lluvia, nieve, cellisca o granizo

primera sucesión (primary succession): la ocupación de una vida vegetal en un área que anteriormente no estaba cubierta por vegetación

productor (producer): un organismo que sintetiza su propio alimento

radiación adaptativa (adaptive radiation): la diversificación por selección natural, a través de tiempo evolutivo, de especies o grupos de especies a muchas diferentes especies que se adaptan regularmente a diferentes nichos ecológicos

rasgo (trait): característica de un organismo que puede ser descrito o medido

recesivo (recessive): se usa para describir el gene que es anulado por un gene dominante; el rasgo está encubierto

red alimenticia (food web): relación compleja formada por cadenas alimenticias interconectadas en un ecosistema representando el traslado de energía a través de diferentes niveles

selección natural (natural selection): la diferencia en supervivencia y reproducción entre los miembros de una población

sésil (sessile; non-motile): un organismo que está permanentemente unido, sin movimiento libre

simetría bilateral (bilateral symmetry): disposición de las partes de un organismo que se divide en dos mitades simétricas, derecha e izquierda

simetría radial (radial symmetry): disposición de las partes de un organismo que tiene simetría sobre el eje central

sucesión (succession): el lento y ordenado reemplazo de la comunidad de reemplazo, una siguiendo a la otra

sucesión secundaria (secondary succession): la ocupación de vida vegetal en una área que estaba cubierta anteriormente por vegetación y que todavía tiene tierra

tasa de crecimiento (growth rate): la proporción a la cual el tamaño de la población aumenta como resultado de la tasa de mortalidad, la tasa de natalidad, la inmigración y la emigración

tasa de mortalidad (death rate – mortality rate): la proporción a la cual las muertes disminuyen el tamaño de la población

tasa de natalidad (birthrate – natality): la proporción a la cual la reproducción aumenta el tamaño de la población

termodinámicas (thermodynamics): el estudio de la transformación de la energía descrita por las leyes

transpiración (transpiration): la emisión de vapor de agua de los poros de las plantas como parte de sus procesos de vida

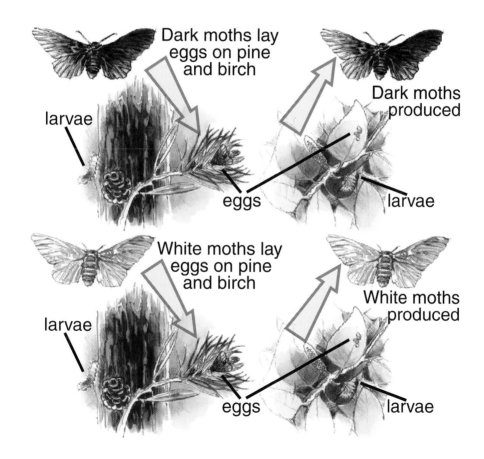

Charts/Graphs/Tables

Annual Rate of Population Growth, 34
Body Symmetry, 87
Carbon Cycle, 67
Changes in Reindeer Population, 32
Comparing Animals, 5
Ecocolumn, 63
Food Web, 19
Generation: Predator/Prey, 100
Human Population Growth Between
    A.D.1-2000, 33
Kinds of Leaves From Germinating Tobacco
    Leaves, 94
Major Divisions of Geologic Time, 115-116
Native Woods Containing Pine and Birch
    Trees, 102-103
Nitrogen Cycle, 72

Number of Families Of Marine
    Organisms Through Time, 121
Number of Families of Terrestrial
    Tetrapods ThroughTime, 122
    Organization in the Biosphere, 8-9
Oxygen Cycle Through
    Photosynthesis and Respiration, 66
Phosphorous Cycle, 74
Pyramid of Energy, 26
Range of Different Species of Brachiopods,
    120
Succession on Krakatoa, 50
Theoretical Pyramid of Living Matter, 28
Water Cycle, 58
Water Temperature Chart, 25

Index

A

Abiotic, 8
Abiotic factors, 26
Adaptation, 8, 82-86
Adaptive radiation, 119, 123
Alien species, 44
Allelopathy, 47
Aquifer, 58
Autotroph, 18, 67

B

Bilateral Symmetry, 87
   Body Symmetry, 87
   Radial Symmetry, 87
Biodiversity, 4, 9-11,
   14-15, 86
   Decrease in, 10
   Importance of, 11-14
Biological amplification, 30
Biotic, 8
Biosphere, 8-9
Birthrate, 36
Body fossil, 113
Body symmetry, 5, 87
   Bilateral symmetry, 5, 87
   Radial symmetry, 5, 87

C

Captive breeding, 108
Carbon cycle, 63-67
Carbon-14, 118
Carnivore, 17, 20, 26
Carrying capacity, 37
Chromosome, 95
Climax community, 53
Community, 9, 27
   Climax, 53
   Pioneer, 53
   Seral, 53
Competition, 22, 40-45
   Evolutionary change and, 43,
      106
Condensation, 58
Consumer, 17, 18, 19

D

Darwin, Charles, 104-105
Death rate, 36
Decomposers, 19-20, 22,
   65-66, 73
Denitrification, 73-74
Dominant gene, 96
   Recessive gene, 96
Domino Effect, 12

E

Ecosystem, 9
Emigration, 36
Energy, 26-29, 66-67
   Pyramid of, 28
   Transfer of, 27
Evolution, 104-106, 113, 123
   Evidence of, 113
   Theory of, 104, 113
Exotic species, 44
Extinction, 10, 15, 38, 119,
   123
   Effects of, 12-14
   Mass, 123

F

Fertilizer, 72, 75
First-order (primary) consumer,
   19, 21-22
Food chain, 17, 18
   Energy and, 26
   Trophic levels in, 29
Food web, 17-20, 22-23
   Alternative pathways in, 20
   Aquatic, 23
Fossils, 109-116
   Body, 113
   Cast, 114
   Formation of, 113-115
   Importance of, 113
   Index, 116
   Trace, 113

G

Gene, 95-96
   Dominant, 96
      Genotype, 92, 96, 98
      Phenotype, 96, 98
      Recessive, 96
Genetics, 95-96
Genotype, 92, 96, 98
Geologic time, 115
Greenhouse effect, 68
Groundwater, 58-59
Growth rate, 36

H

Habitat, 5, 45
Heat stroke, 24
Herbivore, 17-19, 26
Heredity, 93-96
Heterotroph, 18-19
Holyrod, Pat, 26
Hydrach succession, 54
Hydrologic cycle, 58
Hypothesis, 104, 122

I

Immigration, 36
Index fossil, 116
Inference, 122
Infiltration, 58
Inherited, 82, 86, 95
Inorganic nutrients, 67
Introduced species, 44
Invasive species, 44, 47

K

Krakatoa, 49-50

L

Law of thermodynamics, 24,
   27
League of Concerned Voters
   2-3

M

Mass, 28
Mass extinction, 119, 123
Mendel, Gregor, 96
Models, 113
Mortality rate, 36
Mt. St. Helens, 54

N

Natality, 36
Natural selection, 99, 104,
   106-108
Niche, 119, 123
Nitrogen cycle, 68, 71-72
   Agriculture and, 75-76
Nitrogen fixation, 71-73
Nonnative species, 40, 44
   Alien, 44
   Exotic, 44
   Introduced, 44
   Non-indigenous, 44

O

Omnivore, 20
On the Origin of the Species, 105
Opposable thumb, 86
Organism (defined), 9

P

Paleontologist, 116,
Periwinkle plant, 12
Phenotype, 92, 96, 98
Phosphorous cycle, 68, 74-75
   Agriculture and, 75-76
Photosynthesis, 63, 65-66
Pioneer community, 53
Population, 9
   Closed, 37
   Factors affecting size of,
      31-36
   Open, 35-38
Precipitation, 58
Predator, 100
Prey, 100
Primary productivity, 27
Primary succession, 44, 52, 54
Producer, 17-19
Pyramid of energy, 26, 28, 30
Pyramid of living matter, 28
Pyramid of number, 29

R

Radial symmetry, 5, 87
Recessive gene, 96
Respiration, 55, 63, 66
Runoff, 58

S

Second-order consumer, 19, 22
Secondary succession, 48, 52
Seral stages, 53
Species, 9-10, 86, 95
Succession, 48-53
   Mt. St. Helens and, 54
   On Krakatoa, 49-50
   Primary, 48, 52, 54
   Secondary, 48, 52
Sun, 26-27, 58, 67
Symmetry (see Body symmetry)

T

Theory, 99, 104
Thermodynamics, 27
Trait, 92, 95
   Inherited, 92
Transpiration, 55, 60
Trophic level, 28

U

U.S. Government Executive
   Order 13112, 44

W

Water cycle, 55, 57-61
   Aquifer, 58
   Condensation, 58
   Evaporation, 58
   Groundwater, 58
   Human impact on, 60-61
   Hydrologic Cycle, 58
   Infiltration, 58
   Precipitation, 58
   Runoff, 58
   Transpiration, 60
Whitman, Christy Todd, 78

Photos and Illustrations